Physics
IS FUN ———————————————————

An introductory course for secondary schools in four volumes

BOOK TWO

Jim Jardine, *B.Sc., B.Ed., A.Inst.P.*

Head of the Physics Department, George Watson's College, Edinburgh

Illustrated by Geoffrey Salter

Heinemann Educational Books Ltd · LONDON

Heinemann Educational Books Ltd

London Melbourne Toronto Johannesburg Singapore Auckland Ibadan Hong Kong Nairobi

S B N 435 67472 2 (cased edition)
435 67473 0 (loose leaf edition)

First published 1964
Reprinted 1965, 1967, 1968

Published by Heinemann Educational Books Ltd
48 Charles Street, London W.1
Printed in Great Britain at the Pitman Press, Bath

Contents

Preface

Contents

This book covers the second year's work of a Secondary School physics course, following the order of the New Scottish Physics Syllabus (Sections 4–6).

This 'O' Grade Syllabus will be used by a wide range of pupils, and an attempt has been made to cater for the majority of those concerned. It must, however, be appreciated that to any one pupil some parts of the book will appear trifling and other parts extremely difficult. Only the teacher can decide which parts are relevant to the needs of a particular class.

Questions are asked throughout the text. The general aim has been to make them of such a nature that pupils will be encouraged to read the whole chapter and perhaps consult other sources in order to answer the questions. Many of the questions are numbered so that they may be used for written homework.

Although this is essentially a pupil's book, an attempt has been made to combine with it the functions of a laboratory manual and, to a lesser degree, a teacher's guide. Subscripts have been used to indicate suppliers. Their names and addresses are given at the back of the book.

Units

The British system of units has been called 'The Independent British Deterrent'. It certainly has not simplified the teaching of physics. Although there are great differences of opinion regarding the units which should be taught in schools, there is general agreement that too much time has been wasted converting from one system to another.

In Book 1, British and M.K.S. units were used side by side. In this book, M.K.S. units are emphasised more and more, and British units are rarely used. The aim will be gradually to accustom pupils to use only one system of units—the M.K.S. system—when dealing with physical phenomena.

Practical Work

No particular class would ever be expected to take part in *every* experiment described here. Again only the teacher can decide which experiments are appropriate. Many of the experiments can be conducted at home and it is hoped that pupils will be encouraged to carry out some of those as homework projects. Although the practical work has been grouped under three headings, 'experiments', 'demonstrations' and 'models', these are simply intended to suggest a possible presentation. Many teachers will want individual pupils or groups of pupils to conduct experiments labelled 'demonstration'. Sometimes it may be easier to demonstrate some of those labelled 'experiment', but the temptation to do this should be resisted. In general it is proposed that the 'experiments' will be conducted by pupils themselves, either at home or in school. Some of the 'experiments' and 'demonstrations' may be best conducted as 'group experiments'. In order to avoid confusion between a real experiment and apparatus which has been devised to illustrate a principle, the latter will be called a 'model'. It is expected that such models will normally be demonstrated.

It is unlikely that there will be time to write traditional lab. reports of the experimental work—even if this were desirable. Brief results of experiments together with answers to the questions posed can, however, be written in a practical notebook. If the loose-leaf edition of this book is used, pages containing such results may be inserted appropriately.

Thanks

This book has been produced with the co-operation and encouragement of so many people that I find it impossible adequately to express my thanks for all the help received. Friends and colleagues from the physics departments of several schools and colleges read the manuscript and made many helpful comments and criticisms. Experiments 1.8, 1.9, 1.10 and 1.11 were designed by members of the staff of the High School of Stirling.

I am particularly grateful to our lab. technician for making and often designing prototype apparatus, to the artist for his amazing patience and skill in interpreting the spirit of the new syllabus and to the publishers for their enthusiasm and guidance throughout the undertaking.

Finally the entire manuscript was read and criticised by Dr Davidson of Aberdeen University. For the time and trouble he so willingly took I should like to express my sincere thanks.

July 1964   J. J.

Publisher's Note

Question numbers in the text follow the questions thus (*15*).

References in the text to the List of Suppliers appear thus $_{15}$.

Introduction—meet a model

For centuries man has been making models. He has used them to explain complex events or to communicate difficult ideas—in short to 'make sense' of the unfamiliar. Models and analogies are so important in the study of physics that we ought now to consider carefully their value and their limitations.

In the first part of this course we used many models. We studied scale models of motor cars and of the solar system. We examined models of internal combustion engines and hydro-electric schemes. We built models of machines such as the block and tackle and the wheel and axle. These were merely 'small imitations of the real thing'—which is how one lady defined a 'model husband'!

We also used other models, and here we must pay careful attention to the shift in meaning of the word. Small beads were used in the kinetic model designed to help us picture gas molecules. The solar system was proposed as a model of the atom. In such models it is not merely their scale or the material from which they are made that differentiates them from the 'real thing'. These models are more like parables or analogies. They are in no sense 'scale models'. If then such models are quite different from the real thing, what is their value? There are at least three answers to this question. In the first place, they give us a mental picture of something which is outside the range of our sense perceptions. To most of us this is helpful, at least as a mnemonic, even if in our heart of hearts we admit that the image may be false! Secondly, such analogies help us to think constructively and to suggest properties for investigation. It was Fourier's work on thermal conductivity which inspired Georg Simon Ohm to apply similar ideas to the flow of electricity. We may even use models to make predictions, but such predictions must be checked by experiment, for there is no *a priori* reason for their being valid. The wonder is that so many models have been successful in the development of physical theory. Thirdly, models help to 'explain' things. By this we mean that we can interpret phenomena in terms of something with which we are already familiar. When we see dozens of glass beads battering against and moving a light piston, the kinetic theory 'makes sense'. These are all perfectly legitimate reasons for using models in physics. We must, however, continually remind ourselves that the model is *not* the reality, and that we use the model because experiments have shown that in *some ways* the reality behaves like this. *In some ways* molecules behave like glass beads, *in some ways* electrons are like solid particles, *in some ways* the atom is like the solar system.

This book is concerned with three important models: flow, waves and particles. Flow, for most of us, implies the motion of a liquid. It is because there are some, but only some, similarities with this kind of flow that we use the same term for the movement of electric charges and of heat. We will look for such similarities without being shocked if we encounter many differences at the same time. Waves, for most of us, are the things which make bathing in the sea exciting. Their connection with radio waves is purely semantic. In what way do radio waves or light waves resemble 'real' waves? Unless we have good reasons for showing that there are useful similarities we ought not to use the term at all. We must, moreover, be fully aware of the limitations of the wave model. Finally, particles are tiny fragments. Can we then speak of particles of light or electricity? As we 'watch' electrons shooting through a cathode ray tube we may be confronted with the questions, 'Are electrons *really* waves? Are electrons *really* particles?'

This part of the course should help us to see that there is a limit to the validity of any model. If our 'explanations' are to be consistent with experimental results, more than one model may have to be used.

*   *   *

Fluid Flow

In the next three chapters we will investigate (*a*) the flow of liquids and gases, (*b*) the flow of electricity and (*c*) the flow of heat. In fluid flow, molecules move from place to place. In an electric current charged particles move through solids, liquids or gases. Finally, heat energy is transmitted from one place to another

the coloured liquid whirls around. Such flow is said to be turbulent.

Cigarette smoke rises steadily for a while and then becomes turbulent (Fig. 2). Water from a tap can also be seen to become turbulent after it leaves the tap.

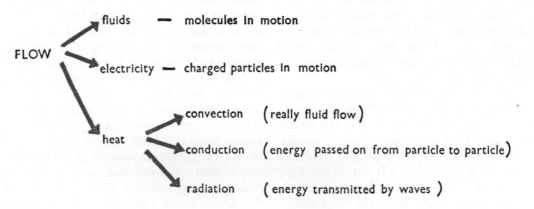

by one or more of three different methods, convection, conduction and radiation.

Streamline (laminar) and turbulent flow

Demonstration 1.1. By injecting a jet of potassium permanganate solution into a tube through which water is flowing, various types of flow may be studied (Fig. 1). The potassium permanganate solution is fed into the water stream through a hypodermic needle [for example a No. 4 serum needle₁] and the rate of flow is controlled by a screw clip. If the water and potassium permanganate are flowing slowly through the tube a fine purple thread can be obtained. This is streamline flow. If the flow rate is increased, the thread begins to break up shortly after leaving the needle and

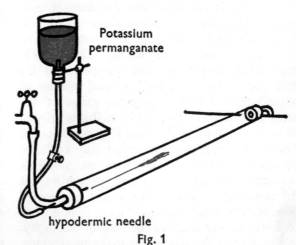

hypodermic needle

Fig. 1

Fluid Flow Round a Body

Demonstration 1.2. By allowing smoke to flow round various bodies the flow patterns

2

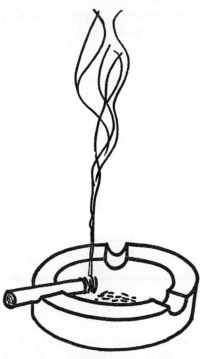

Fig. 2

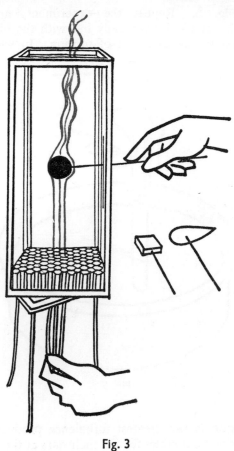

Fig. 3

may be observed. (Fig. 3). A smoke tunnel, about 18 in long fitted with glass sides is suitable. It should have a piece of aluminium honeycomb or wire gauze fitted to the lower end. Three tapers are used to provide the smoke, which is carried gently up the tunnel by convection currents.

Demonstration 1.3. You can study water flowing round a variety of wood blocks, using a sloping tray as shown in Fig. 4. Water is played on the top of the tray from a series of holes drilled every half inch along the brass tube. The water then flows over a number of potassium permanganate crystals which are kept at the top of the tray by a perspex strip. Alternatively the crystals may be held in a folded strip of cheese-cloth. This produces a number of parallel flow lines when there are no blocks on the tray. You should study the effects of placing wood or perspex blocks of different shapes on the tray and note which shapes produce least turbulence.

Experiment 1.4. Pull the blade of a dinner knife quickly through a basin of water as shown

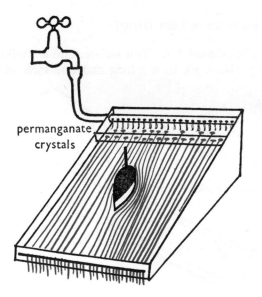

permanganate crystals

Fig. 4

in Fig. 5. Repeat the experiment, again holding the knife vertically but with the blade angled to the direction of motion. In which

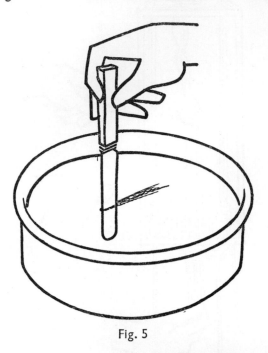

Fig. 5

position is the greatest turbulence produced? Why do boat crews feather their oars at the end of each stroke?

Resistance to Flow (Drag)

Experiment 1.5. You will require a shallow tray about six inches long and one inch wide

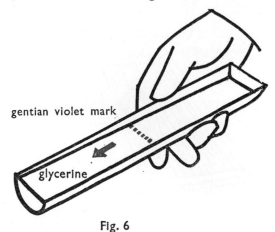

gentian violet mark

glycerine

Fig. 6

for this experiment. A polythene acid bottle sliced down the middle will do very well. Half fill the tray with glycerine and mark a line across the glycerine with the aid of a wire which has been dipped in a solution of gentian violet and glycerine. Gently tilt the tray so that the glycerine flows in the direction indicated. Where is the flow (a) fastest and (b) slowest? Can you suggest why a fluid moves more slowly at the walls of the tube than it does in the centre?

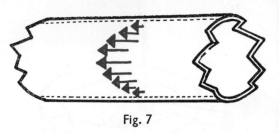

Fig. 7

We can represent the speed of flow by arrows of different lengths. The longer the arrow the greater the speed. At the walls of the container the fluid is stationary and the arrows have shrunk to points.

Demonstration 1.6. The effect of shape on air resistance may be examined using the model, illustrated in Fig. 8. A streamlined balsa wood body is made up of three sections, A, B and C, which can be pinned together. The centre section is supported by a pivoted wire. A vacuum cleaner can be used to direct a jet of air on to the body. It is then pushed over to the left and the scale reading gives an indication of the air resistance (drag). The nozzle of the vacuum cleaner should always be adjusted so that it is parallel to the long axis of the body.

Note the drag produced when all the sections are fitted together. Now remove the nose and replace it with a metal disc of the same weight. Again note the drag. Repeat this procedure with the tail removed and another disc fitted. Why is it necessary to fit these discs?

When is the air resistance (a) greatest and (b) least? Which reduces air resistance more, the addition of the nose or the tail?

Speed, Shape and Surface

Turbulence is produced when fluids flow at high speeds or flow over bodies which are not streamlined. In addition to the speed and shape of the object the nature of the surface can also have an effect on the drag produced. Modifications of the surface, such as the dimples in a golf ball, alter the flow pattern and the drag. As turbulent flow is extremely involved, only streamline (laminar) flow will be studied in the following pages.

Measuring flow

(a) Flow Rate

The rate at which a fluid flows through a tube is measured by a flowmeter. The simplest meter of this kind consists of a tapering tube[2,4] in which a light metal ball acts as an indicator (Fig. 10). As the flow rate increases the ball

from
vacuum
cleaner

Fig. 8

Designers of aircraft, rockets, submarines, boats and cars are all concerned to reduce drag to a minimum. To do this they study the behaviour of scale models in wind tunnels where the effects of turbulence can be investigated. *Can you give examples of streamlined shapes in nature?* (*1*)

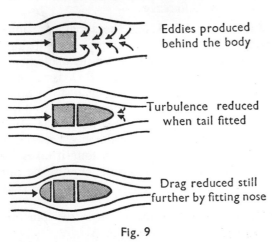

Eddies produced behind the body

Turbulence reduced when tail fitted

Drag reduced still further by fitting nose

Fig. 9

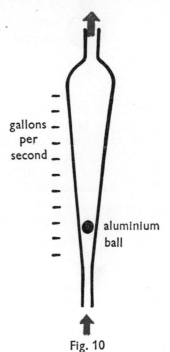

gallons per second

aluminium ball

Fig. 10

rises further up the tube until it is in equilibrium. *How would you calibrate such an instrument?* (*2*) Accurately calibrated instruments suitable for liquids and gases are also available. A Rotameter[24], size 7A fitted with a type A float is suitable for measuring the flow of gas, and a size 10 with a type S float is suitable for water.

A simple flowmeter suitable for measuring the rate of flow of gases may be constructed

In Fig. 12 (ii) the liquid column AC indicates the pressure of the water flowing through the pipe and in Fig. 12 (iii) a Bourdon pressure gauge is used to read the liquid pressure.

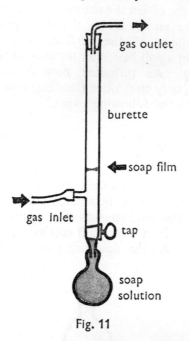

Fig. 11

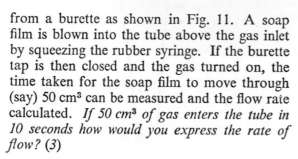

from a burette as shown in Fig. 11. A soap film is blown into the tube above the gas inlet by squeezing the rubber syringe. If the burette tap is then closed and the gas turned on, the time taken for the soap film to move through (say) 50 cm³ can be measured and the flow rate calculated. *If 50 cm³ of gas enters the tube in 10 seconds how would you express the rate of flow? (3)*

(b) Pressure

Earlier in the course you used a manometer to measure pressure. Such instruments normally measure the *pressure difference* between the pressure in a fluid and the atmospheric pressure.

In Fig. 12 (i) the fluid exerts a pressure at A and the atmosphere exerts a pressure at C. As A and B are at the same level the column CB represents the fluid pressure. Strictly speaking we should say 'in excess of atmospheric pressure' but this is usually taken for granted.

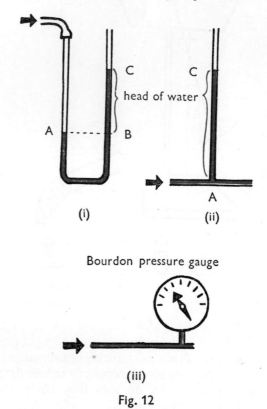

Fig. 12

Factors affecting the rate of flow

1. Pressure Difference

Experiment 1.7. Using the apparatus shown in Fig. 13 adjust the water tap and clip until the pressure difference between the manometers A and D is (say) 5 cm. This P.D. is required to keep the water moving against frictional resistance. Measure the time taken to fill a 500 cm³ measuring jar. Now adjust the water tap so that the pressure difference between A and D is 10 cm and find how long it takes for 500 cm³ of water to flow out. How is the rate of flow affected by increasing the pressure difference?

Draw a graph showing how the pressure varies with the distance from A.

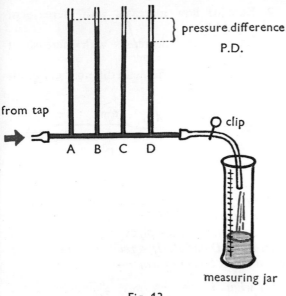

pressure difference
P.D.

from tap

A B C D

clip

measuring jar

Fig. 13

If a calibrated flowmeter is available the rate of flow can be measured directly.

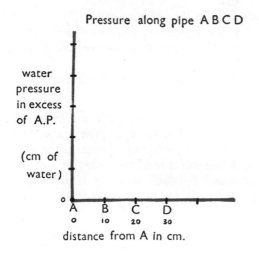

Pressure along pipe A B C D

water pressure in excess of A.P.

(cm of water)

A   B   C   D
0   10   20   30

distance from A in cm.

The pressure of water becomes less and less along the length of the pipe. This fall in pressure per centimetre (say) is called a *pressure gradient*. If the pressure falls by 5 cm of water over a length of 5 cm of pipe it will, on the average, fall by $\dfrac{5}{5} = 1$ cm of water every centimetre of pipe. The pressure gradient is then 1 cm of water per cm.

If the distance between the tubes A and D in Fig. 13 is 30 cm and the pressure difference is 6 cm of water the pressure gradient will be

$$\frac{6}{30} = 0.2 \text{ cm of water per cm.}$$

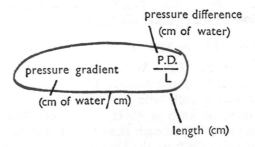

pressure difference (cm of water)

pressure gradient

$\dfrac{\text{P.D.}}{\text{L}}$

(cm of water / cm)

length (cm)

Experiment 1.8. Pressure difference (P_1–P_2). Connect 15 cm of capillary tubing to a 50 cm³ Rocket syringe (Luer mount)$_{25}$ using plastic tubing as shown in Fig. 14. Fill the syringe to the brim with water, making sure that there is

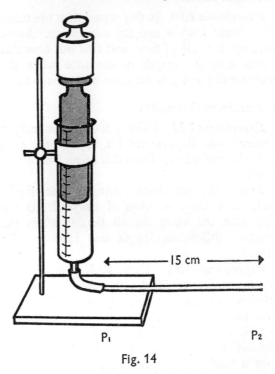

15 cm

P_1 P_2

Fig. 14

no air between the plunger and the water. Place a 200 g mass on top of the plunger and time the flow of (say) 20 cm³ of water through the tube. This may be done by noting how long the plunger takes to move from the 50 cm³ to the 30 cm³ marks.

Repeat the above procedure using a 500 g mass on top of the plunger. How does this affect the pressure difference (P_1–P_2) between the ends of the capillary tube? How has the rate of flow of water been affected?

2. Area of Cross Section (Bore)

Experiment 1.9. With the apparatus of Experiment 1.8 use various 15 cm lengths of glass tubing each with a different bore. For convenience keep a short length of plastic tubing attached to each glass tube and remove the plastic tube from the Luer mount. Measure the rate of flow as before, and thus discover how it varies with the area of cross-section. How would you ensure that the pressure difference is practically the same across each tube?

3. Length of Tube

Experiment 1.10. In this experiment use tubes of different lengths and the same bore. Again measure the rate of flow, and find out how this varies with the length of the tube when the pressure difference is the same across each tube.

4. Stickiness (Viscosity)

Experiment 1.11. Using a 500 g mass and the apparatus of Experiment 1.8, replace the cold water by hot water. Does this affect the rate of flow?

Repeat the experiment, using another liquid such as a weak solution of Polycell. Is the flow rate the same for all liquids when the pressure difference, length and bore are the same?

Experiment 1.12. Drop ball bearings into one measuring jar filled with water and another filled with glycerine. Through which liquid do they fall more quickly?

This method can be used to compare the viscosities of normal and multigrade car oils over a range of temperatures.

Summary

1. Rate of flow increases with increase of pressure difference (P.D.).

2. Rate of flow increases with increase of tube area (A).

3. Rate of flow decreases with increase of length (L).

4. Rate of flow varies with different materials (M).

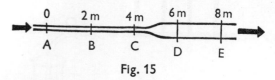

Fig. 15

A fluid flows through a length of narrow tube before entering a wide tube (Fig. 15). Manometers are fitted to the pipes at 2 metre intervals at A, B, C, D and E. If A reads 100 cm of water and B reads 80 cm of water—

(a) *what is the pressure difference across AB?* (4)

(b) *what is the pressure difference across BC?* (5)

(c) *what is the pressure gradient along AC?* (6)

(d) *what is the pressure at C?* (7)

(e) *will the pressure difference across DE be greater or less than the pressure difference across AB?* (8)

(f) *will the rate of flow be greatest at A,B,C,D or E?* (9)

The pressure of a gas supply is 5 in of water. A manometer is fitted to a gas pipe near a gas fire. The manometer reads 3 in of water when the fire is on. What will it read when the fire is off? (10) *What could be done to increase the pressure available at the gas fire when it is in operation?* (11)

Why is a water pump fitted in a central heating system which uses small-bore pipes? (12)

Bernoulli effects with streamline flow

Although it is possible to compress a liquid very slightly it may be assumed for most practical purposes that liquids are incompressible. Hydraulic brakes depend on this property (see Book 1, page 66). *If, therefore, a liquid is flowing through a wide tube, which tapers to a narrow tube, would you expect it to move more quickly in the narrow tube? (13)*

Demonstration 1.13. A piece of 1 in diameter glass tube may be used in this experiment as an air reservoir. Connect one end of it to a water

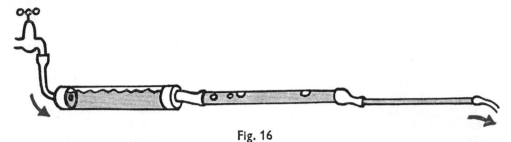

Fig. 16

Demonstration 1.15. Connect the Bernoulli Tube used in the last experiment to the gas supply instead of the water supply, and light the gas coming from each outlet. What do the heights of the flames tell you about the gas pressure in the narrow part of the tube?

tap and the other to a $\frac{1}{2}$ in diameter tube. A narrow outlet pipe should be fitted to the other end as shown in Fig. 16. Turn on the tap and send a bubble of air from the air reservoir through the tubes. Note any change in speed as the bubble passes from the wide to the narrow tube. What can you say about the speeds at which the water is flowing in the two tubes?

A   B   C

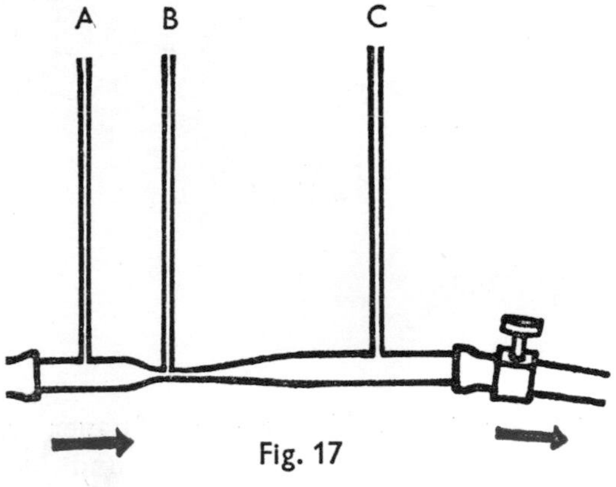

Fig. 17

Demonstration 1.14. Connect up a Bernoulli Tube$_2$ to a water tap, and control the rate of flow with the tap and the outlet clip (Fig. 17). Observe the height of the water in the manometers A, B and C. How do the pressures compare with the pressures obtained in Experiment 1.7? What does this suggest happens to the pressure of the fluid when it speeds up in the narrow part of the tube?

Demonstration 1.16. A series of manometers may be used to investigate the air pressure at a constriction between two metal plates (Fig. 18). The lower plate has a series of holes drilled in it and small metal tubes are soldered round them. Each tube is connected by rubber tubing to a manometer. The apparatus should be mounted on a board so that the upper plate can be adjusted to within an eighth of an inch

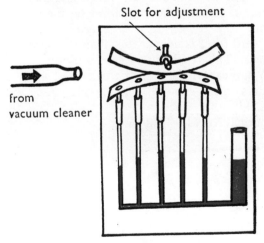

from vacuum cleaner

Slot for adjustment

Fig. 18

of the lower plate. A vacuum cleaner may then be used to blow air between the plates. What happens to the air pressure where the air speed is greatest? Apparatus similar to the above is available commercially$_2$.

When a fluid is forced through a narrow gap the fluid pressure is *reduced* as its speed *increases*. It can be shown by rather difficult mathematics that this must be the case if the total energy of the moving fluid at each point is to remain constant. For the present, however, the following may help to show why the pressure is reduced as speed increases.

Fig. 19

First imagine that you are cycling at a constant speed against a steady head wind. The forward force will be equal to the force of friction plus the wind force (Fig. 19). Suppose now that the wind suddenly drops and that you continue to exert the same force on the pedals. *What will happen to your speed?* (14) The forward force is now greater than the opposing forces. This results in an acceleration.

Your experiments with trucks and speedometers also showed that acceleration was possible only when a force greater than the frictional forces was applied.

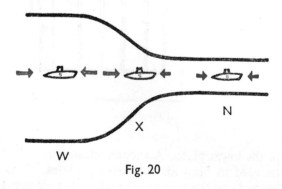

Fig. 20

Imagine a midget submarine S moving with the water in a wide tube W (Fig. 20). It is

moving at a constant speed. *What does this tell you about the force, and thus the pressure, behind it and in front of it?* (15) We will assume that the submarine always moves at the same speed as the water around it. Soon the submarine enters the narrow tube N. *What can you say about the speed of the water, and thus of the submarine, at N compared to its speed at W?* (16) *Why?* (17)

The submarine must therefore *accelerate* at X where it enters the narrow tube. In order to do this the force behind it must be greater than the force in front of it, and this is possible only if the pressure behind it is greater than the pressure in front of it. Thus the pressure in the moving fluid decreases as the fluid speeds up. A Swiss mathematician named Daniel Bernoulli discovered this fact about two hundred years ago. It is called the 'Bernoulli effect'.

Tricks

Here are a few tricks you might like to try to explain in terms of Bernoulli's principle.

Fig. 21

Experiment 1.17. Place a sheet of paper over two books as shown in Fig. 21 and blow through the tunnel thus formed. What happens? Note that with *fast flow* the *pressure is low.*

Experiment 1.18. Hold a sheet of paper as shown in Fig. 22 and blow across the top of it. The high speed air across the surface causes a reduced pressure and the greater atmospheric pressure beneath pushes the paper upwards. Can you explain how a roof can be 'blown off' a house when a gale blows *over* it?

Fig. 22

Experiment 1.19. Place a small piece of card on a cotton reel and insert a pin through it and into the hole in the reel (Fig. 23). Now blow through the reel and explain why the card does not fall off.

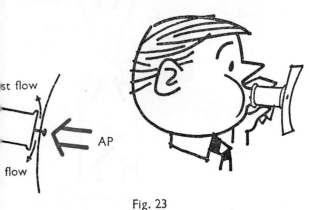

Fig. 23

Experiment 1.20. Why is the table tennis ball held in a stable position by the air blast? (Fig. 24) Think what happens when the ball tends to fall out of the air stream. Can you tilt the tube and keep the ball in the airstream? Is it possible to keep more than one table tennis ball supported at one time by the air stream? What happens if you use a golf ball instead of a table tennis ball?

Experiment 1.21. Pick up a table tennis ball with a vacuum cleaner *blowing* into a filter funnel (Fig. 25). You may place the ball in the position shown first! Can you explain why the ball stays in the funnel?

With the vacuum cleaner switched off invert the filter funnel and place a table tennis ball in

it. Now switch on the cleaner. Is the ball blown out?

You can pick up a table tennis ball without using a vacuum cleaner simply by blowing into a thistle funnel.

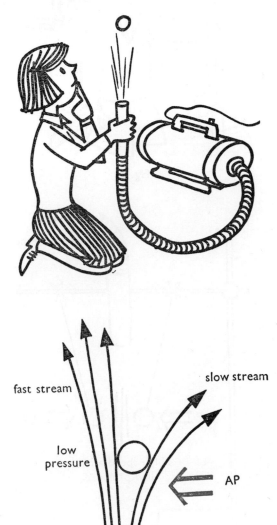

Fig. 24. Conditions which exist if the ball falls to the right hand side.

Experiment 1.22. Blow a jet of air *down* between two table tennis balls which are hanging on threads (Fig. 26). Why do they come together?

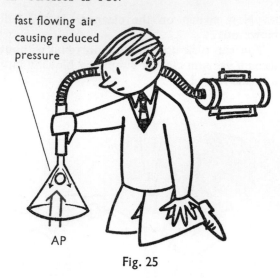

fast flowing air
causing reduced
pressure

AP

Fig. 25

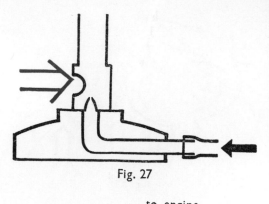

Fig. 27

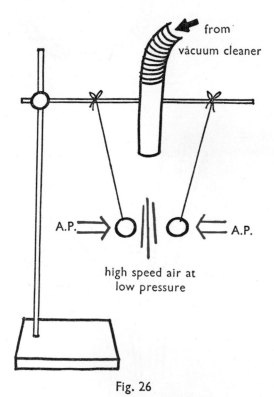

from
vacuum cleaner

A.P. ⟹ ○ ∥ ○ ⟸ A.P.

high speed air at
low pressure

Fig. 26

Application of Bernoulli's Principle

Can you explain how a bunsen burner (Fig. 27) and a carburettor (Fig. 28) operate? (18) Remember that for fast flow the pressure is low.

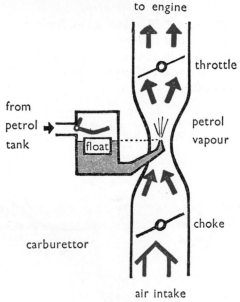

to engine

throttle

from
petrol
tank

float

petrol
vapour

carburettor

choke

air intake

Fig. 28

Why Does a Spinning Ball Swerve?

A cricket ball or a tennis ball can be made to curve rather than go straight simply by giving the ball some spin. This motion is more easily studied with a cardboard cylinder.

Experiment 1.23. Roll one end of a piece of one-inch tape three or four times round a cardboard cylinder and give the other end a vigorous tug as shown in Fig. 29. The spinning cylinder should then be projected forwards. Does it move in a straight line?

The spinning cylinder carries a layer of air around with it. The air in contact with the cylinder is moving at the same speed as the cylinder itself, whilst layers of air further from it revolve more and more slowly.

We can consider a cylinder moving from right to left as if it were a stationary cylinder

Fig. 29

with the air moving from left to right as shown in Fig. 30. Where the air carried round by the cylinder is moving in the same direction as the air through which it is passing (above it) the air speed is increased and therefore, according to Bernoulli's principle, the pressure is reduced. Below the cylinder the pressure is increased

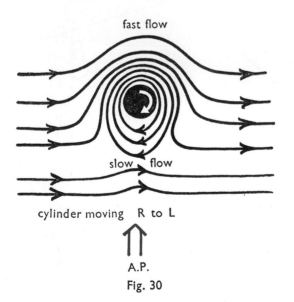

fast flow

slow flow

cylinder moving R to L

A.P.

Fig. 30

because of the reduction in air speed due to opposing air streams. This greater pressure below the cylinder forces it upwards and can even make it loop the loop.

From Fig. 30 you can see that the cylinder is forced in the direction of the movement of its leading edge. In the above case its leading edge (left hand face) is moving upwards and the cylinder is forced upwards. It 'follows its face'.

Fig. 31

Experiment 1.24. Place a table tennis ball in a cardboard tube which is about a foot long and 2 inches in diameter. Swing the tube to project the ball horizontally (Fig. 31). Does the ball 'follow its face'?

An experimental ship once crossed the Atlantic using two rotating cylinders instead of sails. *If the wind were blowing in the direction shown (Fig. 32) would the cylinders have to rotate in a clockwise or anticlockwise direction as seen from above? (19)*

How Does an Aeroplane Fly?

Because of the shape and position of the wing, the air flowing above it has to travel further than the air flowing below it. The air above the wing is therefore travelling more quickly and the pressure is less. The lift thus

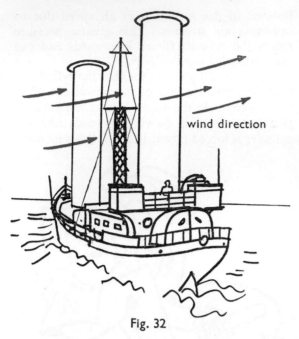

Fig. 32

Even with the most carefully designed aircraft it is not possible to get rid of all turbulence. The boundary layer of air round the wing refuses to come away cleanly with the rest of the flow. It swirls and forms vortices, which are small whirlpools of air. This accounts for much of the drag which reduces efficiency and keeps flying costs high. A great deal of research in aircraft design is aimed at trying to reduce turbulent flow.

Fig. 34

obtained depends on the angle of attack, that is, the angle at which the wing is inclined to the oncoming air flow. As this angle is increased so the lift is increased, but the flow pattern

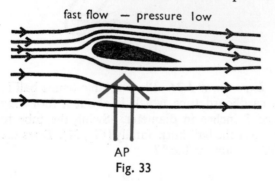

fast flow — pressure low

AP

Fig. 33

Experiment 1.25. Can you explain why the toy rotor illustrated in Fig. 34 rises almost vertically when it is spun rapidly?

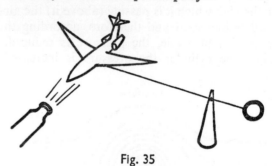

Fig. 35

does not alter appreciably. Beyond a certain angle of attack (the critical angle) the region behind the wing becomes much more turbulent. This destroys lift and increases drag so that the aircraft stalls, as the lift is now too small to support it.

Experiment 1.26. Balance a model aircraft on the end of a rod using a counter-balance weight. It should be free to move vertically. Blow air from a vacuum cleaner past the plane and see how lift is affected by altering the angle of attack.

Visual aids

16 mm Sound Films

20.7313 Aeroplanes: How They Fly[44].
How an Aeroplane Flies. Part 1. Lift[48].

High Speed Flight (Simplified version)[48].
The Power to Fly[48].
Schlieren[48].

Flow of electric charges

CHAPTER 2

Atomic structure

If your sister argued that matter is continuous *what experiments would you use to defend the hypothesis that it is made up of* tiny particles? *(1) If she then insisted that it was nonsense to suggest that these particles were always in motion, what experiment would you show her? (2) Finally could you demonstrate the presence of electric charges on, say, a polythene rod? (3)*
What models of the atom have been suggested to explain the way matter behaves? (4) These were discussed in Book 1, Chapter 6.

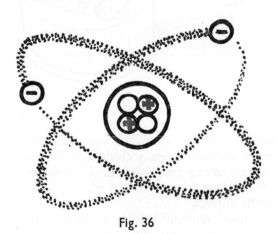

Fig. 36

One model represents the atom as a positively charged nucleus surrounded by negative charges called electrons (Fig. 36). The particles in the nucleus are referred to as *nucleons. If an atom is neutral how will the number of protons in it compare with the number of electrons? (5) What particles, apart from protons, are found in the nucleus? (6) Are they electrically charged? (7)*
In this model of the atom it is assumed that, although the nucleons are tightly bound together, some of the electrons may leave the atom

fairly easily. From the results you obtain in the following experiments you will be asked to decide whether or not this is a useful model.

Electric charges

In order to investigate the behaviour of electric charges you will again have to assume the role of a detective. You will, however, have a very valuable assistant, the electroscope.

Fig. 37

You will be charging objects by (a) rubbing, (b) sharing charge and (c) induction. The electroscope will help you to detect whether or not a body is charged.

Charging by Rubbing

Experiment 2.1. Discharge a polythene rod by waving it over a bunsen flame. Test that it has been discharged by bringing it near an electroscope. Now rub the polythene rod on the plate of the electroscope. The leaves should diverge and stay apart when the polythene rod is removed. What happens to the leaves if the polythene rod is brought back near to the electroscope plate? What does this suggest?

Now charge a cellulose acetate rod by rubbing it with a cloth. What happens when the charged acetate rod is brought close to the plate of the charged electroscope?

The electroscope enables us to detect whether or not a body is charged. In addition we can use it to test whether the charge is like that on the polythene rod (negative) or like that on the acetate rod (positive).

Experiment 2.2.

(*a*) Charge two inflated plastic balloons by rubbing them with a duster. Suspend the balloons on nylon threads and bring them close together. How do they behave? Test the type of charge on each balloon by bringing it close to a charged electroscope. What do you conclude from this experiment? An interesting variation of this experiment is obtained by filling the balloons with coal gas or helium.

(*b*) Devise an experiment to study the effect of bringing together a positively and a negatively charged object.

Demonstration 2.3. In this experiment you can charge a polythene rod by rubbing it with a liquid. Half fill a calorimeter with mercury and place it on the plate of an electroscope. Now discharge a polythene rod by passing it through a bunsen flame. When you are satisfied that the electroscope and the rod are discharged, place the end of the rod in the mercury and then remove it. What happens? Replace the rod in the mercury and note the deflection now. What do the results tell you about the size and nature of the charges produced?

Charging by Sharing

Is an electrically charged body related to an electric current in anything other than name? Can an electric current be detected when a body is being charged or discharged? To help us answer these questions look at the following demonstration.

Demonstration 2.4. Charges on the move. We will use a microammeter in this experiment to indicate current.

Charge the sphere of a Van de Graaff generator, and test that it is charged by bringing an electroscope close, but not too close, to it. Now connect the sphere to a sensitive microammeter, such as a Pye Scalamp₃, as

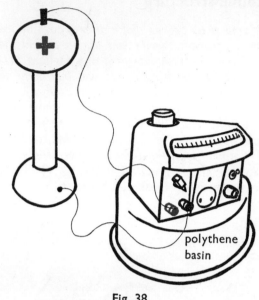

Fig. 38

shown in Fig. 38, and see if you can detect an electric current. Finally check that the sphere has been discharged, using an electroscope.

What does this experiment tell you about an electric current?

A microammeter which measures electric current gives an indication of the number of electrons passing every second. A micro-amp (10^{-6} amp) is a rate of flow of 6 million, million (6×10^{12}) electrons per second.

Experiment 2.5. For this experiment you will require a few calorimeters or tin cans standing on polythene blocks or polystyrene cups and some U-shaped pieces of wire (Fig. 39). Charge an electroscope whose plate is wired to the first can as shown. Note the deflection. Holding one of the U-shaped wires with an insulator gently lower it so that it makes contact with the first and second cans.

Alternatively drop the wire on to the cans. Again note the deflection of the electroscope.

Add the other cans one at a time to the

If a small charged body were connected to a really enormous conductor what would you expect to happen to the charged body? (8)

Fig. 39

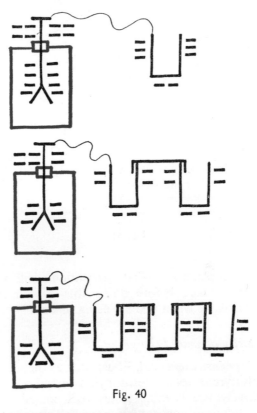

Fig. 40

electroscope and observe the deflection and hence the charge on the electroscope each time.

(Perspex tweezers sold by photographic suppliers are ideal for holding the bent wires.)

When a charged body is discharged an electric current flows. We can imagine this current in most solid conductors to be a flow of electrons. If we then think of a charged body as having a surplus of electrons (negatively charged) or a scarcity of electrons (positively charged) we can see that the electrons move towards or away from the body if it is touched by a conductor. The charge is *shared out* over the conductors. In the above experiment this means that the bigger the conductor (more cans) the smaller will be the charge (number of surplus electrons) on each conductor (can). The total number of surplus electrons remains the same, that is, *charge is conserved.*

Demonstration 2.6. Charge an electroscope, then connect it to a large globe (Fig. 41). Make sure the globe is standing on an insulator. What happens to the charge on the electroscope?

Now connect a charged electroscope to a water tap so that it is connected to the real Earth. Why do the leaves collapse?

Insulators and Conductors

Experiment 2.7.

(a) Touch a charged electroscope with your finger. Does the result suggest that your body allows electrons to flow through it? What else must allow electrons to flow through it?

(b) Try to discharge an electroscope by touching its plate with different materials which you are holding. Use such things as rubber, wool, glass, metals, cork, cloth and

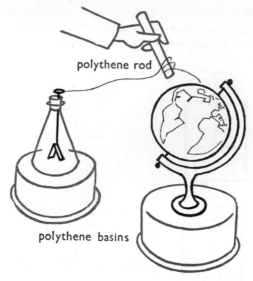

polythene rod

polythene basins

Fig. 41

charged sphere of a Van de Graaff generator what happens? Allow the ball to touch the Van de Graaff sphere so that some of the charge on it is transferred to the ball. What happens now? What can you say about the type of charge on the Van de Graaff sphere and the type of charge transferred to the ball?

Demonstration 2.9.

(a) Place a disc of thin silver paper on top of a Van de Graaff dome and switch on the generator. Explain the result.

(b) Attach a metallised polystyrene sphere to the top of a Van de Graaff dome, using a fine silk thread. Note the result when the Van de Graaff generator is switched on.

various plastics. What precautions will you have to take before doing this experiment, particularly when you are using plastics?

Polarity of shared charge

Demonstration 2.8. Suspend a metallised polystyrene sphere$_2$ on a nylon thread. Alternatively use a table tennis ball coated with Aquadag. If now you bring the ball close to the

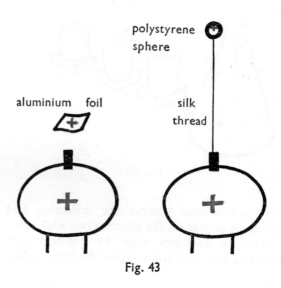

polystyrene sphere

aluminium foil

silk thread

Fig. 43

Fig. 42

Demonstration 2.10. Support two gongs from electric bells on polythene rods and suspend a metallised polystyrene ball (or table tennis ball) between them. Now connect up the gongs to the Van de Graaff generator as shown (Fig. 44) and explain what happens.

Demonstration 2.11. Fix a metal plate inside a clear plastic tumbler and attach it to the dome of a Van de Graaff machine with a 4 mm plug. Put a few metallised polystyrene spheres inside the tumbler and switch on the generator. The balls are charged by contact with the metal plate.

should be connected to the base of the generator as shown in Fig. 46.

Fill the tube with smoke from a smouldering taper and place a piece of polythene on top of the tube to prevent its escape. Switch on the Van de Graaff. Why does the smoke disappear? Can you think of an industrial application?

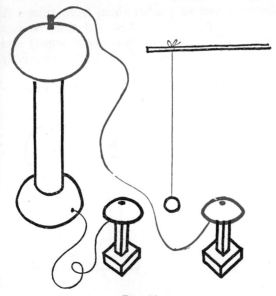

Fig. 44

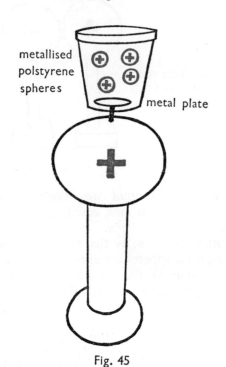

metallised polstyrene spheres

metal plate

Fig. 45

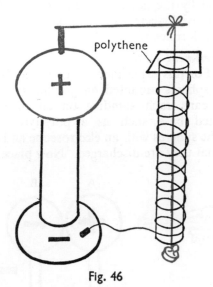

polythene

Fig. 46

Charging by Induction

Demonstration 2.13. Connect one terminal of a sensitive galvanometer to a water tap and

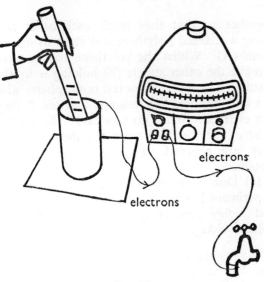

electrons

electrons

Fig. 47

Demonstration 2.12. Attach a heavy wire to the dome of a Van de Graaff machine and hang a fine wire from it. Let the fine wire pass through a wide glass tube round which a few turns of wire have been wound. This wire

the other to a calorimeter standing on a piece of polythene (Fig. 47). Now plunge a charged polythene rod into the calorimeter and note the galvanometer deflection. What happens when the polythene rod is removed?

In the last experiment electrons were repelled by the polythene rod so that a current was detected by the galvanometer. When the rod was removed electrons flowed back from earth to the calorimeter.

Experiment 2.14.

(a) For this experiment you will require two metal spheres mounted on polythene, or two small cans each standing on an uncharged insulated base such as a polystyrene cup. Test the spheres with an electroscope and make sure that they are discharged. Now place them

electrons and so pushes them from sphere A to sphere B. Sphere B would thus have a surplus of electrons (negatively charged) and sphere A a scarcity of electrons (positively charged).

The spheres are said to have been charged by induction.

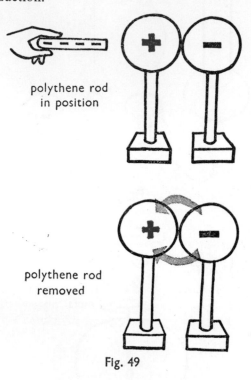

polythene rod
in position

polythene rod
removed

Fig. 49

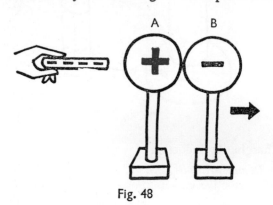

A   B

Fig. 48

together so that they touch each other and bring a charged polythene rod close to one of them (A). Whilst the polythene rod is there remove the other sphere (B) holding it by the insulating support. Now test both spheres with a partly charged electroscope and see if they are charged. What do you find? Touch the spheres together and again test them to see if they are charged. Explain the results you obtain.

(b) Discharge the spheres and repeat the experiment but this time remove the polythene rod *before* separating the spheres. Are the spheres charged?

The results obtained in the above experiment can be understood by assuming that the negatively charged polythene rod repels some

Notice carefully that we obtain not *one* induced charge but *two* equal and opposite induced charges. Those charges neutralise each other as soon as the polythene rod is removed if the spheres are allowed to remain in contact. Only if the spheres are separated whilst the polythene rod is still there can they be charged.

Experiment 2.15.
Place a calorimeter on the plate of an electroscope (Fig. 50). Charge a polythene rod and bring it close to a small stream of water so that water drops are directed into the calorimeter. Are the water drops charged? Do they carry the same type of charge as the polythene rod? Can you explain this, remembering that water is an electrical conductor and the tap is earthed?

Fig. 50

The negatively charged polythene rod repels electrons in the metal bar and so pushes them to the other end, which therefore becomes negatively charged. This charge is shared with the ball so that it is repelled from the metal bar and carries with it a surplus of electrons, that is, a negative charge.

Experiment 2.17. Repeat the last experiment, but in place of the polystyrene sphere allow the plate of an uncharged electroscope to touch the end of the metal bar (Fig. 52).

Fig. 52

Experiment 2.16. Charge a polythene rod and bring it close to the end of a metal bar mounted on an insulator. Suspend a metallised polystyrene sphere$_2$ by a nylon thread and allow it to touch the other end of the metal bar. What happens when it touches the bar?

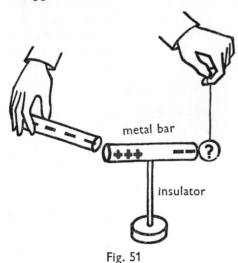

metal bar

+++ --- ?

insulator

Fig. 51

Now use a partly charged electroscope to test the charge on the polythene rod and the charge on the sphere. Are they the same or different?

Now move the electroscope away from the bar whilst the charged polythene rod is close to the other end. Has the electroscope acquired a charge?

Remove the polythene rod and allow the electroscope to touch the metal bar again. What happens, and what does the result tell you about the charges on the electroscope and the metal bar?

Experiment 2.18. Bring a negatively charged polythene rod close to an uncharged metal bar as shown (Fig. 53). Some of the electrons in the metal bar will be pushed away towards the end. Now touch the bar, momentarily, with your finger before removing the polythene rod. Test the metal bar to see if it is charged and if so what type of charge it has.

Repeat the experiment, touching different parts of the bar each time. Is the metal bar left charged if you touch the end nearer the polythene rod?

In this experiment some of the electrons repelled by the polythene rod are conducted to earth through your body. The metal bar is therefore left with a scarcity of electrons, that

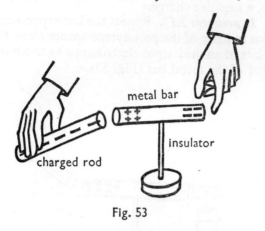

metal bar

insulator

charged rod

Fig. 53

is, a positive charge. Note that the bar is left with the *opposite* type of charge to that on the rod. What is the result of removing the polythene rod before taking your finger off the metal bar?

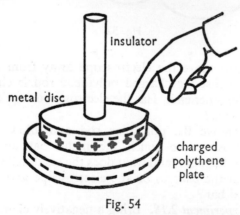

insulator

metal disc

charged polythene plate

Fig. 54

Experiment 2.19. Attach a rod of perspex or polythene to the centre of a brass disc. Alternatively you can fix a candle to the inside of a tin lid using candle wax. Now charge a flat piece of polythene, or a polythene plate, by rubbing it with a duster. Place the lid on the plate and momentarily touch the lid with your finger. When you now lift the lid off the plate

you will find that it has acquired a strong charge. Such a device is called an electrophorus.

Electrons are pushed away from the negatively charged polythene plate and some of them escape to earth when the lid is touched. What kind of charge would you expect to find left on the lid? Test your answer using an electroscope.

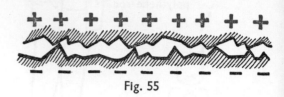

Fig. 55

A microscope photograph of the surface of the polythene plate might look like Fig. 55. Because the metal plate actually touches the polythene plate at only a very few points, there is practically no movement of charge from the polythene to the metal plate whilst they are charged and in contact. As polythene is such a good insulator the other charges on its surface cannot flow to the contact points.

Experiment 2.20. Use an electrophorus to charge someone who is standing on a polythene basin. Ask him then to touch a wire connected to one terminal of a Scalamp galvanometer. The other terminal should be earthed. Explain the observed result in terms of a flow of electrons.

Charging an electroscope

If a negatively charged polythene rod is brought close to the plate of an electroscope and the electroscope plate is earthed (for example, by touching it), electrons will be repelled to earth as shown in Fig. 56(a). If now the finger is removed from the plate while the polythene rod is still near it (Fig. 56(b)), the positive charges will be attracted by the negative charges on the rod. They will therefore remain on the electroscope plate and the leaves will not diverge.

If the polythene rod is now removed, the positive charge will spread over the electroscope plate, rod and leaves. The leaves will therefore diverge (Fig. 56(c)).

Notice carefully that the electroscope has acquired the *opposite* type of charge to that on the polythene rod.

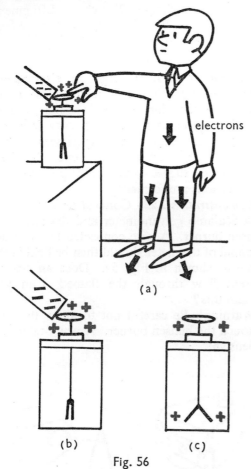

(a)

(b)   (c)

Fig. 56

Summary

Methods of Charging

There are three important ways by which objects can be charged electrically.

(i) *Rubbing*. Electrons leave certain materials more easily than others, so that one of the objects rubbed becomes charged positively and the other negatively.

(ii) *Sharing*. When a charged conductor comes in direct contact with an uncharged conductor, the charge is shared.

(iii) *Induction*. When a charged body is brought close to an uncharged conductor, electrons in the conductor are attracted or repelled. It is possible to charge the conductor by induction if it is (a) split in two or (b) earthed momentarily while under the influence of the charged body.

Flow of charges in a gas

Fields

We have found that some forces act at a distance. The force which draws an apple to the Earth is called a gravitational force. *Does this force draw the Earth towards the apple?* (9)

The force which draws the *north pole* of one magnet towards the *south pole* of another is called a magnetic force.

Thirdly we found that certain materials were attracted to or repelled by each other when rubbed with wool or cotton. We called this type of force an electric force and said that the materials had been electrically charged. The type of charge on polythene we called a negative charge.

These three types of action-at-a-distance forces are often referred to as *field forces*. We speak about a gravitational field, a magnetic field and an electric field.

It is possible to build screens, such as metal boxes, which will prevent magnetic and electric fields from penetrating, but no one has yet discovered a method of 'screening' gravity.

How would you detect (a) a gravitational field, (b) a magnetic field and (c) an electric field? (10) If your detector gave no indication what would this mean? (11)

Electric Fields

When charged soap bubbles were blown towards the sphere of a Van de Graaff generator they tended to move along the dotted lines shown in Fig. 57. Such lines are sometimes referred to as *lines of electric force*. They indicate the direction in which the force acts on a charged particle at any point. *Can you draw a diagram showing the lines of gravitational force round the Earth? (12)*

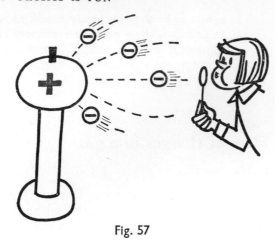

Fig. 57

Ionisation

If a gold leaf electroscope is charged negatively as shown (Fig. 58) and left standing, the leaves do not collapse, yet they are surrounded by air molecules which are free to move. If some gas molecules were positively charged particles and others negatively charged we would expect the positive particles to move towards the leaves and thus cancel the charge. The leaves would then fall. As they do not fall this suggests that normally gas molecules are not charged. They are electrically neutral.

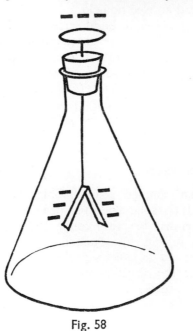

Fig. 58

Under certain conditions, however, one or more electrons (negatively charged) can be knocked off an atom which is therefore left with a positive charge. The charged fragments are called *ions*. *To what kind of charged body will a positive ion be attracted? (13) What will attract electrons? (14).*

Experiment 2.21. Charge an electroscope negatively and bring a lit match close to its plate. The flame ionises the air so that charged particles can move towards or away from the electroscope. Repeat this experiment with a positive charge on the electroscope. Do these experiments suggest that both positive and negative ions are formed?

Demonstration 2.22. Connect an h.t. battery to a Scalamp galvanometer and the base of a bunsen burner. A wire connected to the other terminal of the meter should then be held in the flame as shown in Fig. 59. Does an electric current flow through the flame? Can you explain this?

Warning! Be careful not to allow the wire to touch the bunsen burner. A new Scalamp is expensive!

Scalamp

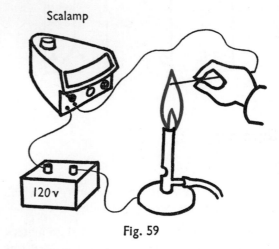

120v

Fig. 59

Demonstration 2.23. Place two metal plates at either side of a bunsen flame and connect the plates to a high voltage power unit. Use a car headlamp bulb to project a shadow of the flame on a screen as shown in Fig. 60. How does the shadow change when the h.t. supply is switched on? Does the flame move towards both plates? Does this suggest the presence of both positive and negative ions in the flame?

and the other to the negative terminal of the source, there is a large pressure or *potential difference* (that is, a high *voltage*) between the electrodes. Gradually reduce the pressure in the tube and observe any changes that take place.

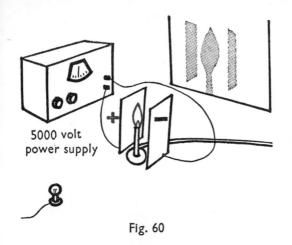

Fig. 60

Demonstration 2.24. Connect an electroscope to a brass plate as shown in Fig. 61 and charge them until the leaves diverge. Pass an electric current through a Nichrome wire coil placed

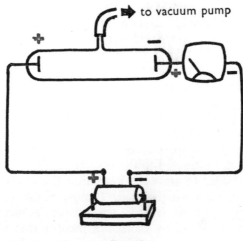

to vacuum pump

Fig. 62

Is there a current (*a*) through air at normal atmospheric pressure? (*b*) through air at reduced pressure when a high voltage is applied?

The gas discharge tube

If the tube is fitted with two metal plates (electrodes), one at either end as shown in Fig. 63, a potential difference (voltage) may be

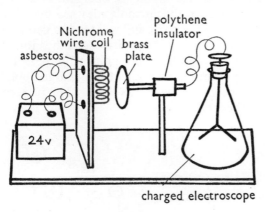

Fig. 61

close to the brass plate. What happens to the charge when the wire glows red? Why? Does it matter if the plate and electroscope are charged negatively or positively?

Ionisation by high voltage

Demonstration 2.25. Connect a discharge tube to an induction coil using a 0–5 mA milliammeter to indicate any current. If one electrode is connected to the positive terminal

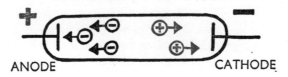

ANODE   CATHODE

Fig. 63

applied across the tube. The electrode to which the positive terminal of the supply is connected is called the *anode*, and that to which the negative terminal is connected is called the *cathode*.

It is usual for at least a few ions to be present in a gas—possibly due to ionisation by the cosmic rays or radioactivity normally present to a certain extent. Let us suppose that one free electron is present in a low pressure gas. If a small potential difference (say 100 volts) were applied across the electrodes, the electron would move towards the positive electrode without being detected. If a large potential difference (say 30,000 volts) were applied, the electron would have a much greater force exerted on it. It would therefore speed up more rapidly. If this fast-moving electron collides with an atom it can ionise it, that is, knock off one or more of its electrons. This process may be repeated with the newly released electrons thus producing still more electrons . . . This process is called an avalanche process. In these collisions positive ions are also produced. They are attracted to the negative plate.

In order to start the ionisation the electron has to reach a high speed. If most of the air is not pumped out (that is, the pressure reduced) there are so many molecules present that the electron keeps bumping into them so that it never reaches a high enough speed. *Why does reducing the pressure make the avalanche process possible? (15)*

Demonstration 2.26. Study discharge tubes filled with neon, sodium or mercury vapour at low pressure. Such tubes may be operated from a small induction coil, a high voltage transformer or power pack.

Warning! Do not stare at an ultra-violet source such as a mercury vapour tube.

What gases do you think are present in the discharge tubes used to light our streets? (16) Fluorescent lighting uses discharge tubes. Some of them give about three times as much light as a tungsten bulb using the same amount of electrical energy. *What happens to the additional energy consumed by the tungsten bulb? (17)*

Ionisation at a sharp point
Demonstration 2.27.
(a) Connect a Wimshurst machine or a Van de Graaff generator to a sharp pointed object. Now place a lit candle near the point and start up the machine. What happens to the flame?

(b) Attach the Van de Graaff to an electro-static 'windmill' and see what happens when it is charged.

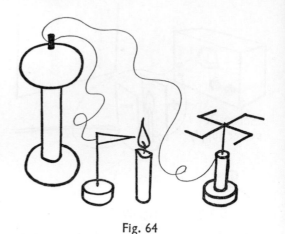

Fig. 64

Electric charges tend to pile up on a sharp point so that there is a very strong electric field near it. If the point is charged positively, electrons from the air molecules nearby will be attracted to the point and will tend to neutralise the charge on it. The positive ions thus formed will be repelled from the point (Fig. 65). It is the repulsion of such ions from charged points which produces the results observed in the above experiments.

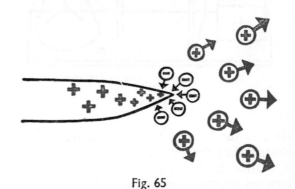

Fig. 65

Notice that charged particles, having the *same sign* as the point itself, carry charge away from the point. For this reason the charge is sometimes said to be 'sprayed' from the point.

If the field is strong enough, that is if the potential between the point and the surroundings is great enough, the stream of ions may start an avalanche process and ultimately a spark will be produced.

Induced charge at a point

An induced charge at a sharp point can ionise the air near it so that charged particles flow through the air to or from the point. The following experiment shows that such electric charges can flow through the air and through your body.

Demonstration 2.28. Ask someone to stand on a polythene basin and hold a sharp-pointed metal object (for example, a nail) in one hand and a wire connected to a sensitive galvanometer in the other hand. The other terminal of

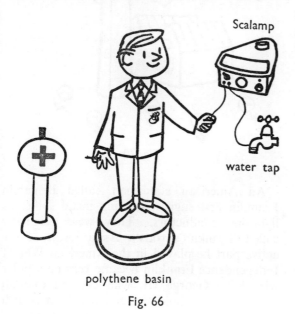

Fig. 66

the galvanometer should be earthed. If the pointed object is brought towards a charged Van de Graaff generator, current will flow through the galvanometer. How is the current flowing between the dome and the point?

Experiment 2.29. Lay a needle on the plate of an uncharged electroscope and bring a charged polythene rod close to it as shown in Fig. 67. Can you explain what happens?

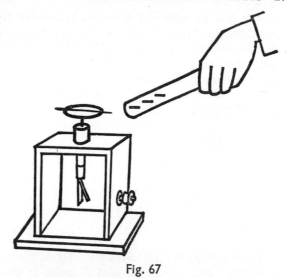

Fig. 67

Van de Graaff generator

In a Van de Graaff generator charges from a high voltage source are 'sprayed' on to an insulating belt which carries them up to the

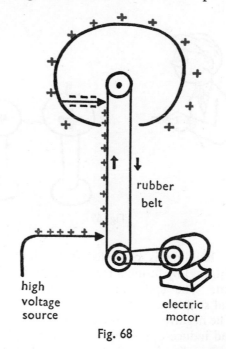

Fig. 68

dome (Fig. 68). The charges are transferred from the belt to the dome by means of a series of points (combs). As a positively charged sphere will repel other positive charges, the motor has to supply the energy necessary to push the additional positive charges towards the dome. This energy is stored as electrical potential energy. The dome is said to have a large *potential* with respect to earth.

There are many modifications to this simple type of Van de Graaff machine, but all of them use sharp points to transfer the charges to and from the belt.

Lightning conductors

Charged conductors can be at least partially discharged by bringing a pointed object close to them.

Demonstration 2.30. Set up a Van de Graaff generator and sphere so that a spark is produced as shown in Fig. 69. Now slowly bring a pointed metal object towards the Van de Graaff dome. Why does the spark disappear? If you bring the point very close to the dome a spark will be produced between it and the point.

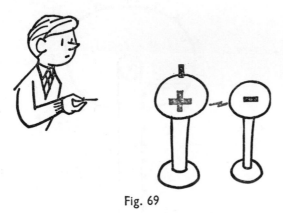

Fig. 69

A building is protected from giant sparks (lightning) by fitting a metal spike to its highest point. The spike must be connected by a metal strip to earth.

The negative charges on the base of a thunder cloud induce opposite charges in the spike and the ground underneath the cloud as electrons are driven away. Charged air molecules then carry off the charge from the spike to neutralise the thunder cloud. If, however, a lightning flash from the cloud does take place, the conductor will lead it safely to earth. If there were no lightning conductor, the thundercloud might discharge violently to the top of a high building or tree causing great damage.

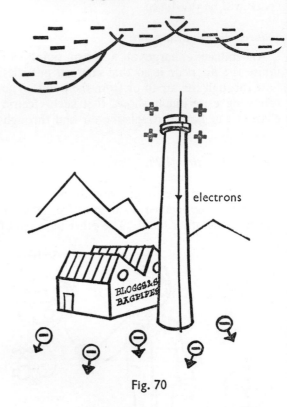

electrons

Fig. 70

An American statesman called Benjamin Franklin first suggested using metal spikes as lightning conductors. They were originally called 'Franklin's rods'. As a result of the active part he played in the American War of Independence Franklin became very unpopular with King George III, who ordered that all pointed rods should be removed from British powder magazines and from his own palace. They were to be replaced by blunt ones. As a result of this incident the following lines were written—

While you, great George, for knowledge hunt,
And sharp conductors change for blunt,
The nation's out of joint.
Franklin a wiser course pursues
And all your thunder useless views
By keeping to the point!

Summary of ionisation

A gas may be ionised by

  (i) a flame

  (ii) a heater coil

  (iii) a high voltage across a gas at low pressure

  (iv) a high charge density at a sharp point.

Thermionic emission

Demonstration 2.31. A diode valve consists of a heater coil (filament or cathode) and a plate (anode) enclosed in an evacuated glass tube.

Connect an h.t. power pack to a simple diode such as the Teltron planar diode₅. A milliammeter should be used to detect the current. With switch 1 open, close switch 2 and note

the milliammeter reading. Now reverse the 400 volt supply and read the milliammeter again. Since the valve is evacuated the only connection between the anode and the cathode is the glass envelope. Is there an electric current through (*a*) the glass, (*b*) the vacuum?

Close both switches and note the reading in the meter when the high voltage supply is connected as shown in Fig. 71. Finally reverse the 400 volt supply, close both switches, and note the meter reading. Can electric charges flow through a vacuum? If so, under what conditions? Why is this tube called a valve?

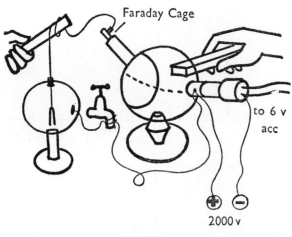

Fig. 72

Demonstration 2.32. Charge on electrons. A Perrin tube₅ is used in this experiment to determine the charge on the cathode rays (electrons) emitted from a hot filament.

Connect a discharged low-capacity electroscope to the 'Faraday cage' as shown (Fig. 72). The case of the electroscope, the anode of the Perrin tube and the *positive* terminal of an h.t. power unit (2,000 volts) should be connected to earth. As the *negative* terminal of the h.t. unit must be connected to the heater, accumulators should be used to provide the 6 volt heater supply. Bring a magnet towards the side of the tube until the electron beam is deflected *into* the Faraday cage. What happens to the electroscope leaves? What does this indicate?

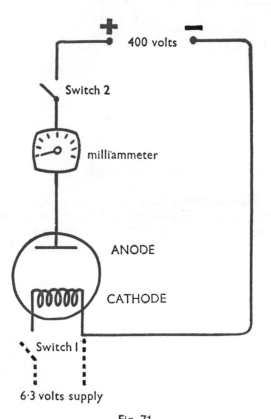

Fig. 71

Remove the lead from the top of the electroscope while the electrons are flowing into the Faraday cage. Can you think of any way to test the charge on the electroscope, assuming that a charged ebonite or polythene rod is negative? Carry out this test and state whether electrons are positively or negatively charged.

so the negatively charged electrons will move across the tube. This flow of electrons through the tube is registered on the milliammeter in the anode circuit (A1). *Would you expect the same current through the meter A2?* (*18*) Test your answer by experiment.

These experiments show that electric current

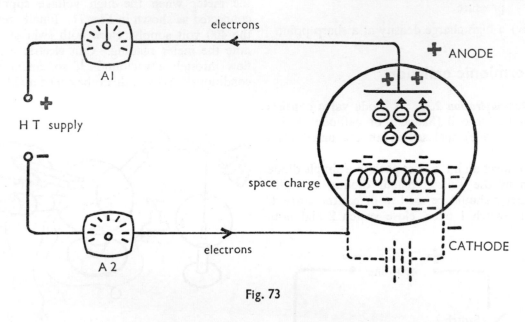

Fig. 73

From the first of these experiments it is clear that a current flows through the vacuum in a diode only when the filament is heated. Even if the filament is hot, current does not flow unless the plate is connected to the positive terminal and the filament to the negative terminal of the battery.

From the second experiment we see that whatever is flowing through the tube carries negative charges. These negative charges (electrons) can only have come from the filament when it was heated. When a metal is heated strongly some electrons actually leave the metal and form a kind of cloud (space charge) round it. If now the plate (anode) is connected to the positive terminal of a high voltage supply and the filament (cathode) is connected to the negative terminal, an electric field will exist between the electrodes.

Just as the charged soap bubbles moved in the electric field of the Van de Graaff generator

can flow through gases by the movement of ions and through empty space by the movement of electrons.

Flow of charge in liquids

Demonstration 2.33. Half-fill a crucible with potassium iodide crystals and insert two carbon rods as shown in Fig. 74. Complete the circuit and see if the bulb lights up. What does this suggest?

Now remove the rods, put the lid on the crucible and heat the potassium iodide until it melts. Replace the rods and continue heating for a short time, as the cold rods may cause some of the potassium iodide to solidify. Does the bulb now glow? What does this tell you?

Remove the bunsen burner and allow the liquid to solidify. What happens to the current? How has the resistance of the potassium iodide altered?

When the potassium iodide crystals are fairly cool, add a few drops of water to the crucible and see if the bulb glows again. What does the result indicate?

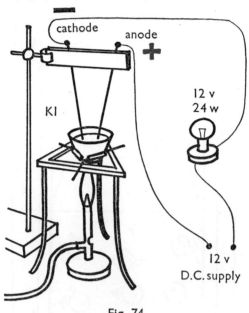

Fig. 74

The potassium and iodine ions are locked in the crystals of the potassium iodide when it is solid. As the ions are not free to move around, electric current cannot flow through the crystals. In the liquid state the ions are relatively free to move so that the liquid is a better conductor of electricity.

The potassium ions are positively charged and move to the cathode which is negative. The

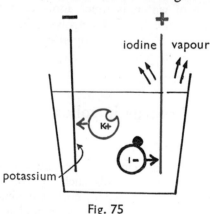

Fig. 75

iodine ions are negatively charged and move to the anode. This accounts for the violet fumes of iodine vapour which are given off at the anode (Fig. 75). Adding water to the crystals forms a *solution* in which the ions are again relatively free to move.

Demonstration 2.34. The above demonstration may be conducted using lead bromide instead of potassium iodide (Fig. 76). In this case you may remove the bunsen burner before inserting the carbon rods. Can you identify the lead (metal) and the bromine (vapour) produced?

As lead bromide is not readily soluble, adding water to the cold salt will not make the bulb glow again.

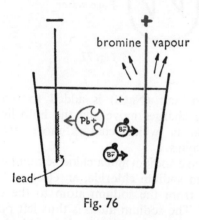

Fig. 76

Experiment 2.35. Charge an electroscope and see if it can be discharged by touching its plate with a strip of cotton or nylon when it is dry and when it is soaked in various liquids such as water, oil, glycerine, methylated spirits and carbon tetrachloride.

Experiment 2.36. Connect a circuit as shown in Fig. 77, using two carbon rods in pure water. Does the bulb light? Now add salt slowly to the water and stir the solution. What do you see and smell?

An electric current will not flow easily through pure water. Although the water molecules are free to move about they do not seem to move towards either plate. *What does this tell you about the molecules?* (19)

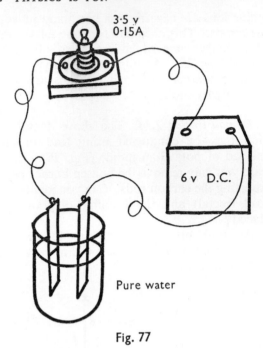

3·5 v
0·15A

6 v D.C.

Pure water

Fig. 77

A similar effect may be obtained with solutions of acids, alkalis or salts. If copper sulphate is used, it is found that, when an electric field is applied, the copper ions (Cu^{++}) move towards the negative plate or electrode and the sulphate ions (SO_4^{--}) move towards the positive electrode. *Which electrode becomes electro-plated? (20) What type of charge do the metallic ions carry? (21)*

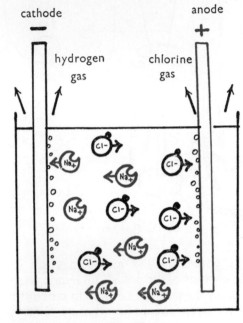

cathode

anode

hydrogen gas

chlorine gas

Fig. 78

When salt (NaCl) is added to the water, electric charges move and the bulb lights up. Liquids in which charges move are called electrolytes.

When a sodium and a chlorine atom combine to form sodium chloride, an electron is transferred from the sodium atom to the chlorine atom. The sodium atom is thus left positively charged (a positive ion) and the chlorine atom becomes negatively charged (a negative ion). In the solid state the ions are held together by electrostatic attraction. In an aqueous solution the force of attraction is reduced and the ions are free to move around.

When an electric field is applied, the chlorine ions (−) move towards the anode (+), where they *lose* electrons and are released as uncharged atoms of chlorine gas, (Fig. 78). The electrons then move on round the external circuit.

The sodium ions (+) move towards the cathode (−), where they *gain* electrons and become neutral atoms of sodium metal. This reacts violently with water giving off hydrogen gas and producing, in solution, sodium hydroxide—an alkali. Can you suggest a test for an alkaline solution?

This process is called electrolysis. With aqueous solutions the process, because of the presence of water, is much more complicated than suggested here. Electrolysis, in addition to being used for electroplating, is used to produce hydrogen and oxygen gases and also to refine metals.

Flow of charge in solids

Experiment 2.37.

(a) Charge an electroscope and try to discharge it through solids such as iron, brass, aluminium, rubber, wood, cork, carbon, polythene, glass, string, paper, cloth and a pencil sharpened at both ends. List the solids you find to be good conductors and those that are good insulators.

2·5 v   0·3 A

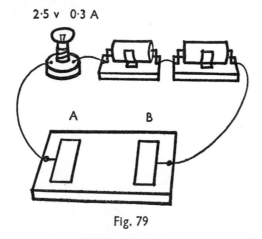

Fig. 79

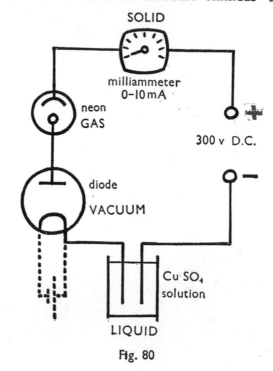

SOLID

milliammeter
0–10 mA

neon
GAS

300 v D.C.

diode
VACUUM

Cu SO$_4$
solution

LIQUID

Fig. 80

(b) Wire a battery and bulb circuit as shown in Fig. 79. Now place the solids you used in the above experiment across metal strips connected to terminals A and B. Again list the good conductors and good insulators. Is the list the same as before? Why is this?

Suitable cell holders are available commercially.

Solid-Liquid-Gas-Vacuum

Demonstration 2.38. Wire up the circuit illustrated in Fig. 80. In this experiment charges are moving, that is, there is an electric current when positive or negative ions move in the liquid ($CuSO_4$) or the gas (neon). In the vacuum (diode) the current consists of moving electrons. In solids both positive and negative charges *can* move but in metallic conductors, such as the wires of this circuit, the current consists of moving electrons.

Plus to Plus

All meters should be treated with great care and respect. The terminals of ammeters and voltmeters for use in D.C. circuits are marked plus and minus. These labels simply tell you how to wire them up. The positive terminals should be connected either directly, or through switches, rheostats, bulbs, etc., to the positive battery terminal. If you wire a meter the wrong way round, the needle will probably 'wrap itself round the stop' and the damage caused may amount to several pounds. You

Fig. 81

should therefore always ask your teacher to check a circuit containing such an instrument *before* you switch on. The meter terminal marked + is saying 'Connect me (eventually) to the positive terminal of the battery'. The negative meter terminal pleads 'Connect me (eventually) to the negative battery terminal'.

Experiment 2.39. Connect up the circuit shown in Figs. 82 and 83 and read the current in each of the meters. What can you say about the current (rate of flow of charge) in such a circuit?

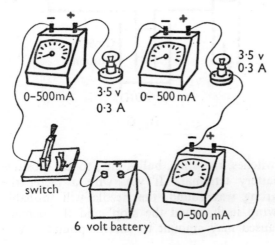

Fig. 82. Practical circuit

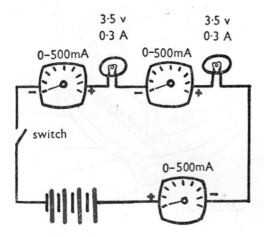

Fig. 83. Theoretical circuit

Experiment 2.40. Assemble the circuit shown in Fig. 84. The full-scale deflection (f.s.d.) for each meter is indicated. Insert only the bulb marked 3·5 V 0·3 A into its holder and read the current in all the meters. Draw a circuit diagram marking the current in the 5 meters.

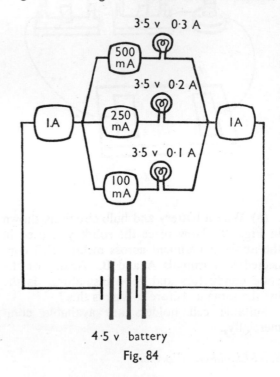

Fig. 84

Now add the 3·5 V 0·2 A bulb so that both bulbs light up, and read all the currents. Draw a second diagram and mark in the currents in each meter. Finally add the third bulb and mark the currents in a third diagram.

What does this experiment tell you about the currents in the three branches and in the main circuit?

Imagine a traffic census being taken near a road junction, such as that illustrated in Fig. 85. It is found that on the average one car per second passes along road P, two cars per second along road Q and three cars per second along road R. Then, if we assume that all the roads are one way streets, six cars per second on the average must pass along road S. *Why is this so?* (22)

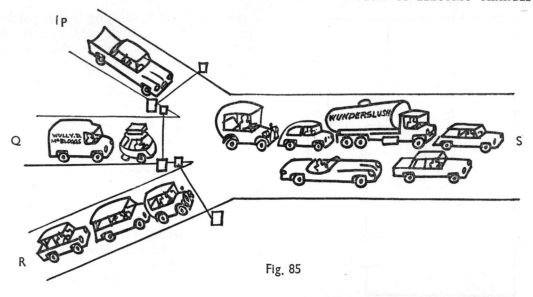

Fig. 85

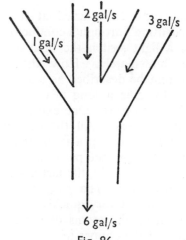

6 gal/s
Fig. 86

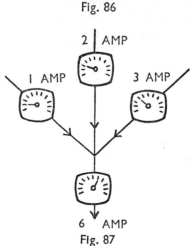

6 AMP
Fig. 87

In the second illustration, Fig. 86, water flows through three pipes at average rates of one gallon per second, two gallons per second and three gallons per second, so that provided there are no leaks in the pipes, six gallons per second must flow through the main pipe.

We have seen from the last experiment that, in this respect, electric current behaves like a flow of water (Fig. 87), so that if one electron per second flows in one branch, two electrons per second in another and three electrons per second in a third branch, the total current will be six electrons per second in the main circuit. In practice electric currents usually consist of millions of electrons passing a given point every second so that we use a unit of approximately six million million million (6×10^{18}) electrons per second and call it the *ampere*.

Problem

From what you know about the behaviour of electric currents can you suggest how the circuit shown in Fig. 88 could be used as an adding machine to add together three numbers? (23) This is really a simple kind of analogue computer.

Free Electrons in Metals

In insulators all the electrons whizzing around the nucleus are bound to it by strong forces so that they cannot easily escape. In

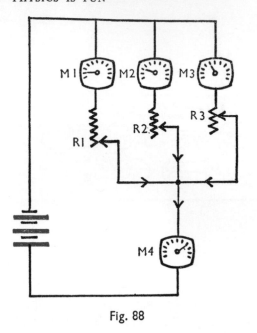

Fig. 88

average they will be drifting in one particular direction at 1 cm/s. If we consider each rat as carrying 1 unit of charge then there is a drift of charge of 1,000 units travelling at 1 centimetre per second.

The above picture is not entirely fanciful, for the average drift velocity of the electrons through a wire is of the order of 1 cm/s, whereas the electrons themselves rush around much more quickly. Their average speed is about 200 miles per second. This analogy, like all analogies, must not be taken too far. You must never try to argue from an analogy. You cannot, for example, say that rats cannot run at 200 miles per second; therefore this is an impossible speed for electrons. The picture is meant to illustrate only the difference between random velocity and drift velocity, nothing else.

You may now be puzzled at the idea of electrons 'drifting' through a conductor. When you press a light switch the light appears to come on immediately. How then can an electric current be described as a slow drift of electrons? Imagine a long pea shooter completely filled with peas. One extra pea is now pushed into one end. All the peas are thus pushed along and one pea is ejected from the other end. Although the peas move along the pea shooter quite slowly, the last pea is ejected almost immediately. The *peas* drift but the *effect* is transmitted very quickly.

Electrons from the atoms of the electrolyte in a battery, of the copper in a conductor and of the tungsten in the filament of a lamp are all identical. It makes no difference, then, which electrons flow in any particular part of a circuit. The fact that there is such a flow means that electrical energy is being transmitted along the conductor. In empty space electrical energy is transmitted at the speed of light, 186,000 miles per second, but in copper wires the speed is about 20,000 miles per second. If a battery were connected by wire to a bulb 20,000 miles away the bulb would light up one second later. It would not, however, be the electrons from the battery which would be flowing through the bulb. The current would have to flow for hundreds of years for this to happen!

metals some of the electrons are so loosely attached to the nucleus that we can picture these electrons moving around freely rather like the molecules of a gas. Free electrons in a metal move in a random fashion, that is, by and large as many electrons move upwards as downwards, to the left as to the right, and so on. If, however, we connect the metal bar to the terminals of a battery the picture is altered as the electrons are now in an electric field. There is, therefore, in addition to the random electron movements, a slight pull towards the positive plate of the battery. This pull causes a 'drift' of electrons, towards the positive battery terminal, of about 1 cm/s when a voltage of a few volts is applied to a thin wire. It is this electron drift which we call an electric current.

Here is an analogy which may help you to understand what is happening. Consider an old barge on a shipping canal. It is packed with (say) 1,000 rats and they are all furiously running hither and thither and getting nowhere. If now the barge starts to drift very slowly in one direction at, perhaps, 1 cm/s then the rats are moving, on the average, at 1 cm/s in one direction. Of course, all the rats may be running at a very high speed all the time but on the

Direction of Current

An electric current may be considered as a flow of negative charges (electrons) in one direction or a flow of positive charges in the opposite direction. We will usually represent it as a flow of electrons, particularly when dealing with electric current in wires. Black arrows will then be used to indicate flow of electrons. When dealing with the movement of positive charges the arrows will be coloured red.

Factors affecting the rate of flow of electric charge (current)

1. Potential Difference

Experiment 2.41. In this experiment you should investigate how the current through the bulb varies when the electrical pressure difference across it is altered. The pressure difference is usually referred to as a potential difference

(P.D.), and is measured in volts using a *volt-meter*. With very large voltages (hundreds of volts) a gold leaf electroscope may be used to measure potential difference, but it is not sufficiently sensitive for circuits like this. The charge on the electroscope varies as the potential difference across it varies. For small voltages a moving-coil voltmeter is used.

Using the circuit shown in Fig. 89 attach one dry cell to the circuit. Note the current in the ammeter and the potential difference across the bulb as measured by the voltmeter.

Now connect two cells in series (positive of one to negative of the next), then three cells in series, each time noting both the current through the bulb and the potential difference across it. How does the current through the bulb vary as the potential difference is increased?

2. Area of Cross Section

Experiment 2.42. Take three carbon rods of equal length and different cross sectional areas and attach one end of each rod to a brass strip. If small brass plates and terminals are attached to the other ends also, better connections can be made. Wire up the circuit as shown in Fig. 90. Attach the wire to the end of the thinnest carbon rod (A) and note the current. Now move the wire to B and then to C, noting the current each time. How does the current alter as the cross-sectional area of the carbon is increased? Which conductor offers most resistance to the current?

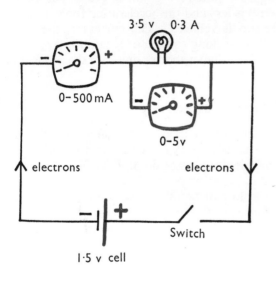

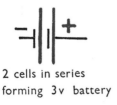

2 cells in series
forming 3v battery

Fig. 89

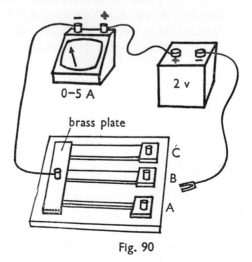

Fig. 90

3. Length

Experiment 2.43. Assemble the circuit illustrated in Fig. 91, using two 1·5 V cells and a 2·5 V 0·3 A bulb. The circuit should be completed through a crocodile clip attached to a length of 30 gauge Nichrome wire held as shown. Slide the clip along the wire and report on any change in current you observe. Does the current increase as the length is increased? Does the resistance increase as the length is increased?

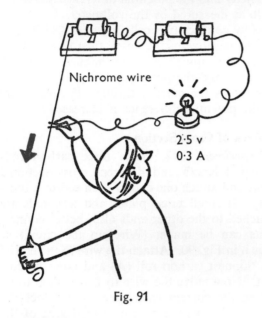

Nichrome wire

2·5 v
0·3 A

Fig. 91

4. Material

By completing a simple battery and bulb circuit with various materials (Experiment 2.37) you discovered that some materials allow electrons to flow quite easily, while others do not.

Summary

1. Electric current increases as the potential difference increases (P.D.).
2. Electric current increases as the cross-sectional area increases (A).
3. Electric current decreases as the length increases (L).
4. Electric current depends on the material of the conductor (M).

Micro Picture

The free electrons in a conductor behave rather like gas molecules. Whenever an electric field is applied to a conductor, a force is exerted on its free electrons and they are therefore accelerated. The greater the voltage applied, the greater will be the electric field and the greater will be the force exerted on the electrons. The current will therefore increase.

When electrons are accelerated they have more kinetic energy. This energy comes from the electric field. As the accelerated electrons make their way through the conductor they bump into the atoms of the conductor, losing the kinetic energy they gain between bumps. This energy is transferred to the atoms and results in heat being produced.

If the cross-section is large, there will be more free electrons available to pass a given point in the conductor every second. The current therefore will be greater. If a conductor is long, the potential gradient (volts per centimetre) is less and the accelerating force on each electron is reduced. The current is therefore smaller. A long conductor is said to have more *resistance* than a shorter one with the same area of cross-section.

Transfer of energy

Electricity is used to transfer energy from place to place. It is in fact one of the most convenient means of doing this. We have seen that in some ways an electric current behaves like a flow of liquid. Here is another analogy to illustrate this similarity.

Imagine that it is necessary to transmit energy from a steam engine to a factory. It would be possible, although not very practicable, to use a system of water pipes as shown in Fig. 92.

The engine drives a rotary pump which pumps water round the circuit. The water then operates a turbine, which in turn drives the machinery in the factory. A manometer across the pump indicates the pressure difference (P.D.) and various flowmeters indicate the rate at which water is flowing. When the circuit branches as shown, the total flow rate (12 gallons per second) is equal to the sum of the

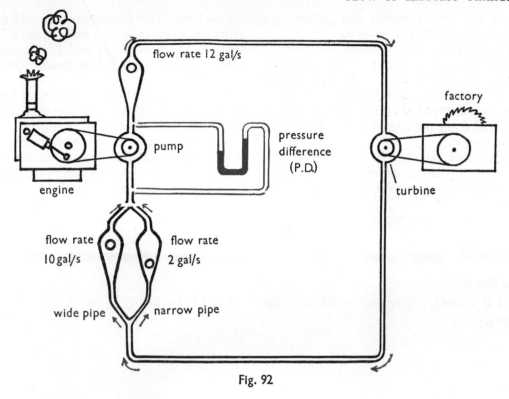

Fig. 92

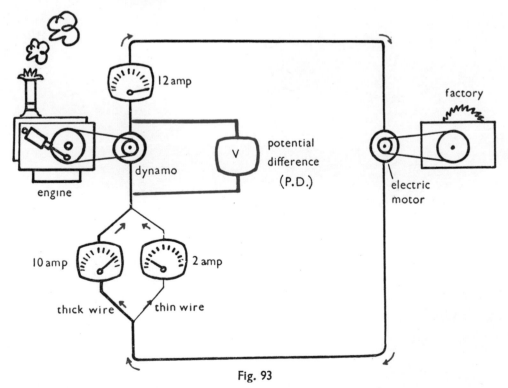

Fig. 93

rates in the two branches (10 gallons per second and 2 gallons per second).

When the water flows through the pump it is given some extra energy. This energy is transmitted by the water through the pipes and operates the turbine which in turn supplies the factory with mechanical energy. Thus energy is transmitted from the engine to the factory by *water in motion*.

Energy could, however, be transmitted much more easily by using an electric circuit. A dynamo replaces the pump, an electric motor the turbine. The flowmeters are replaced by ammeters which read the rate at which electrons are passing (in amperes) and a voltmeter will now read the potential difference (in volts) across the dynamo.

When the electric circuit branches, the total flow (12 amp) is equal to the sum of the currents in each branch (10 amp and 2 amp).

Energy has again been sent from the engine to the factory but this time it has been transmitted by electrical means. Energetic electrons have been pumped round the circuit.

Visual aids

16 mm Sound Films

21.7470 Basic Electricity—Electrostatic Charge.44

What is Electricity?49

Flow of heat

CHAPTER 3

Convection

Heat energy is transmitted from one place to another by three different means. They are called *convection, conduction* and *radiation.*

Convection is really a flow of fluid, that is, a liquid or a gas. In many cases it resembles flotation, but in convection we are dealing with a fluid floating in a fluid rather than a solid floating in a fluid.

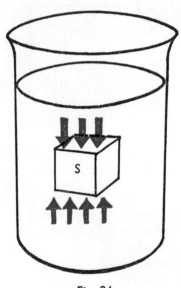

Fig. 94

Imagine a cube of water (S) in the middle of a large beaker of water at rest (Fig. 94). As the cube is in equilibrium the force below it pushing it up must be greater than the force pressing down on it from above. If this were not so, the cube of water would sink because of its weight.

If the space (S) were filled with cork the forces acting above and below would be the same as before, since these forces are exerted by the rest of the water, which has not been altered. The weight of the cork would, however, be *less* than the weight of the water it replaced. The cork would therefore be pushed upwards.

Suppose you were in a space ship where there was no gravitational attraction; would the cork rise to the surface? It is impossible to conduct such an experiment in the laboratory but you can obtain very similar conditions.

8th FLOOR

Fig. 95

Imagine that you were standing holding a tray in a lift at the top of a high building when the cable snapped. The lift and you would fall with the same acceleration, so that if you were to release the tray it would remain in the same position in the lift. If you had not realised that the cable had broken, you would come to the conclusion that the force of gravity had suddenly disappeared. You would be in a state of 'weightlessness' similar to that of an astronaut in a space capsule. This is a somewhat expensive way of finding out if a cork floats to the surface of water in the absence of gravity. Fortunately we need not go to this trouble.

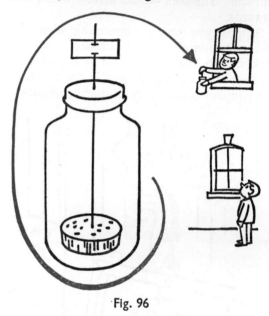

Fig. 96

Experiment 3.1. Find a large glass bottle with a wide neck and a screw top. Drill a half inch hole in the middle of this cap. Now place a large cork in the bottle and stick a knitting needle in it as shown in Fig. 96. Fill the bottle with water, screw on the cap and attach a piece of white tape to the top of the needle to act as an indicator. Push the cork to the bottom of the bottle and see that it is perfectly free to rise quickly to the surface. Now drop the bottle from the window of a two-storey building, making sure that the cork is at the bottom of the bottle when you release it. It would also be advisable to prepare an area of soft soil or sand into which the bottle can fall! Does the cork rise to the surface as the bottle

falls? It is then gravity which is responsible, indirectly, for flotation and convection.

Experiment 3.2.

(*a*) Fill a balloon with coal gas, tie the neck and release the balloon.

(*b*) Use a large light-weight polythene bag as a hot air balloon. A narrow strip of cardboard glued round the neck will keep it open. Place the bag above, but not too close to, a bunsen burner.

Explain why the balloon and the bag rise. If they don't explain why they don't!

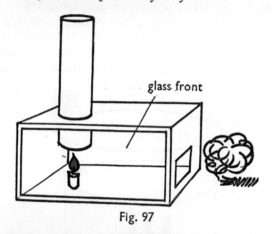

glass front

Fig. 97

Experiment 3.3. A model chimney can be constructed from a glass tube and a cardboard box. Use adhesive tape to fit a sheet of glass to the front of the box. Place a lit candle below the tube and allow smoke to enter a door cut in the side of the box. Explain why the smoke moves in the direction observed.

Experiment 3.4. Cut a spiral from a piece of cardboard, and mount it on a length of wire attached to a candle or bunsen burner as shown in Fig. 98. Why does it rotate? Many rotating toys and Christmas decorations operate on this principle. The imitation flames that flicker in imitation coal fires are produced by a (real) disc which rotates by convection currents.

Experiment 3.5. Place a little fine aluminium powder in a test tube and pour in some benzene or a weak solution of liquid Lux. When the aluminium has settled, gently heat the test tube by holding it by the bottom and observe the result.

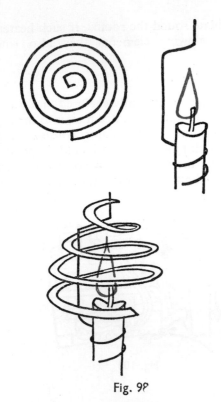

Fig. 98

Experiment 3.6. Fill an ink bottle with hot coloured water and stopper it as shown in Fig. 99. Now lower the bottle into a large beaker of cold water and watch the path of the hot water.

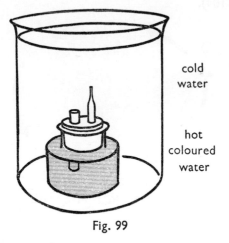

cold water

hot coloured water

Fig. 99

Demonstration 3.7.

(a) Fill one gas jar with hot water and another with cold coloured water. Put a cover over the jar of cold water, turn it upside down and place it on top of the other jar. Now quickly remove the cover and see how the coloured water moves.

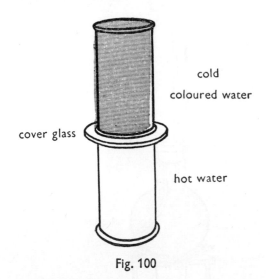

cold coloured water

cover glass

hot water

Fig. 100

(b) Repeat this experiment with hot coloured water in the upper jar and cold clear water in the lower one. Can you explain the difference between the results observed in this and in the previous experiment?

Demonstration 3.8. Construct a model hot water system as shown in Fig. 101 and fill it with a weak solution of liquid Lux containing some fine aluminium powder. The movement of the convection currents can be seen by the movement of the aluminium particles.

Alternatively add potassium permanganate to the reservoir *after* heating has started.

We have seen that when a liquid or a gas is heated it expands. It therefore becomes less dense. The hot fluid is forced upwards by the cooler denser fluid which flows down under it and lifts it up.

Applications of Convection Currents

Heating of Buildings

Most buildings are heated by convection currents. Hot water pipes and 'radiators' heat the air close to them. The hot air then rises and circulates round the rooms. *Why are walls often badly marked above 'radiators'?* (*1*) The

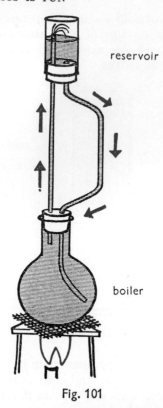

reservoir

boiler

Fig. 101

circulation of the hot water in the pipes is itself sometimes caused by convection, though electric pumps are often used to increase the speed of circulation.

convection

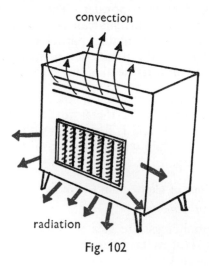

radiation

Fig. 102

Many modern gas and electric fires are convectors, that is, they heat the air and allow it to circulate round the room. If such heaters have red glowing elements they also emit radiation.

Car cooling system

A car engine is normally enclosed in a water jacket. As the water is heated it rises to the top of the radiator. The radiator consists of a series of small pipes past which cold air passes, thus cooling the water. As it cools the water falls to the bottom of the radiator and then returns to the engine.

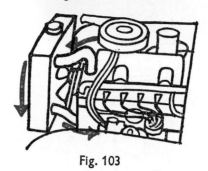

Fig. 103

Sea breezes

During the day the sun's rays fall equally on land and sea. The land, however, warms up much more quickly than the sea. The air in contact with the land soon warms up and rises, while the cooler air comes in from the sea (Fig. 104).

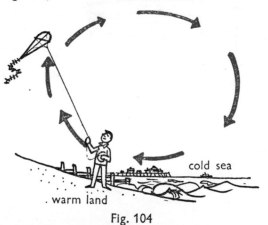

cold sea

warm land

Fig. 104

At night the land loses its heat very quickly while the sea tends to retain its heat. If the sea is now warmer than the land the air in contact with it will be warmed. It will therefore rise as the cool air currents flow out from the land.

Problems on convection

If you were fitting an immersion heater to a water tank would you place the element near the top or bottom? (2) Why? (3)

Can you explain why smoke flows up a chimney? (4)

How does convection affect the ventilation of a room in which a coal fire is burning? (5)

Explain why a 'deep freeze' keeps food cold even when the lid is open, yet a thermos flask does not keep tea warm if the cork is removed. (6)

Conduction

If you have ever picked up a hot saucepan by its metal handle, or taken a hot poker from a fire, you will be aware that heat travels through metals. Often saucepans and pokers have plastic or wooden handles, as heat does not travel so easily through those materials. On a very cold day you will find that if you pick up a plastic and a metal object, both of which are at the same temperature, the metal object feels colder. This is because it takes away heat from your hand more easily than the other. We say that metals are good conductors of heat. You have already found that metals are also good conductors of electricity.

When a metal bar is heated at one end the particles vibrate more vigorously. These particles then bump into their neighbours further along the bar and so cause them to speed up too. As this process goes on heat is being conducted along the bar. Heat energy, in the form of kinetic energy of the particles, is thus being passed on from one particle to the next.

Heat Conduction in Solids

Demonstration 3.9. In this experiment we are going to study the temperatures at different parts of a copper bar when one end is heated. The $\frac{3}{4}$ in diameter copper bar has a copper calorimeter attached to either end and four holes in the bar to hold thermometers. Boiling water is poured into one calorimeter and kept boiling with a bunsen burner. Ice-cold water is poured into the other calorimeter.

A piece of asbestos prevents radiation from the burner reaching the rest of the bar.

Note the thermometer readings once they are reasonably steady and plot a graph showing how the temperature varies with distance from the hot end of the bar.

How does this graph compare with the graph you made showing pressure against distance for water flowing through a glass tube? Can you suggest a reason for any difference you observe?

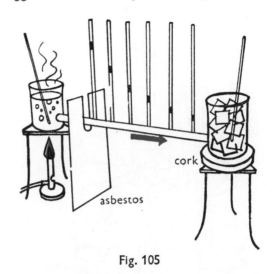

Fig. 105

Factors affecting the rate of flow of heat through a metal bar

1. Temperature Difference

If heat flows into ice at 0°C the ice melts. If more heat is absorbed by the ice, more ice melts. In the following experiments we are going to collect the water produced as ice melts and use it as an indication of the quantity of heat flowing into the ice.

Demonstration 3.10. The apparatus, illustrated in Fig. 106 consists of an asbestos stand into which two calorimeters are fitted. 10 in lengths of $\frac{1}{2}$ in copper bar are brazed into the calorimeters and their ends dipped into funnels containing small pieces of ice. Two bunsen burners heat the calorimeters, one of which contains water and the other dibutyl phthalate. Lengths of glass tubing are fitted into corks on the calorimeters to act as air condensers to prevent the liquids' boiling away. A 0–100°C thermometer indicates the water temperature and a 0–350°C thermometer the temperature of the dibutyl phthalate.

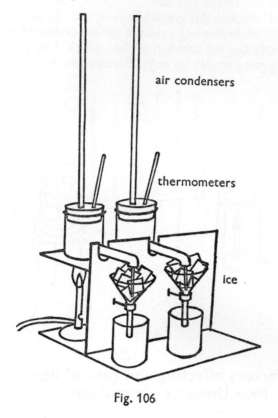

air condensers

thermometers

ice

Fig. 106

Fill the funnels with small ice chips and light the bunsen burners. Maintain the water temperature at 100°C and the dibutyl phthalate at 250°C for about a quarter of an hour. During this time the ice level should be maintained and the funnels agitated occasionally to make sure that ice is kept in contact with the copper rods. Once ice is melting at a fairly steady rate in both funnels, empty the containers and replace them. Note the rate at which ice is melting in each funnel. Across which bar is the temperature difference greater? In which funnel is ice melting more rapidly? What factors are the same for each bar? What does this experiment tell you about the *rate* at which heat flows through a copper bar?

2. Area of Cross Section

Demonstration 3.11. The apparatus, for this experiment may be constructed from a solid brass cylinder (1½ in diameter and 1 in deep) into which two 12 in lengths of copper rod are screwed. Suitable diameters for the rods are ¼ in and ½ in. They should be bent as shown in Fig. 107 and covered with asbestos cement or tape to reduce the loss of heat to the atmosphere. The apparatus may be supported on an asbestos box which contains a bunsen burner to supply heat to the central block. About 2 in of each rod dips into a filter funnel under which an empty beaker is placed.

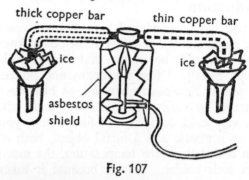

thick copper bar   thin copper bar

ice   ice

asbestos shield

Fig. 107

Light the bunsen burner and fill both funnels with small pieces of ice. Leave the apparatus for about ten minutes to allow heat to travel along the rods. The ice by this time should be melting at a constant rate. The temperature difference across each bar is also constant and we say the apparatus is operating under 'steady state' conditions.

Top up the funnels with ice and place two empty containers below them. Does the ice melt at the same rate in both funnels? Agitate the ice from time to time to ensure that it is making good contact with the bar. Through which bar is the rate of flow greater?

3. Length

Demonstration 3.12. The apparatus used to investigate the effect of length on the rate of heat flow is similar to that used in the previous experiment, except that two ½ in diameter bars are used. Suitable overall lengths for the bars are 10 in and 15 in (Fig. 108).

Leave the apparatus running for some time until 'steady state' conditions exist. As before top up the funnels with ice and place empty containers below them. Through which bar is the rate of heat flow greater?

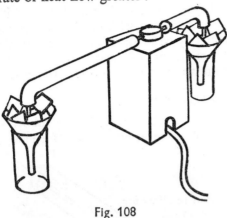

Fig. 108

4. Material

Demonstration 3.13. To study the rate of heat flow through different materials similar apparatus is again used but the length and cross-sectional area of each rod must the same. 12 in rods of copper and iron with ½ in diameters are suitable.

Through which metal is the rate of heat flow greater?

Summary

1. Rate of heat flow increases as the temperature difference increases (T.D.).
2. Rate of heat flow increases as the cross-sectional area increases (A).
3. Rate of heat flow decreases as the length increases (L).
4. Rate of heat flow depends on the material used (M).

CAN YOU EXPLAIN?

Here are a few experiments which you should do yourself. Try to explain what happens in each.

Experiment 3.14. Hold a piece of wire gauze with tongs above a bunsen burner. Now light the bunsen burner below the gauze. What

happens? Turn out the bunsen and relight it above the gauze. Can you explain what happens now?

Why is a paraffin heater for use in garages fitted with a wire gauze?

What is a Davy safety lamp and what is it used for?

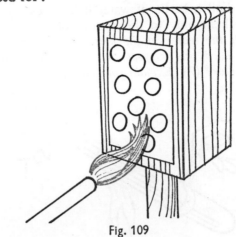

Fig. 109

Experiment 3.15. Press a few drawing pins into a block of wood and then stick a white gummed label over them. Allow a bunsen flame to play on the paper for a few seconds and explain the result.

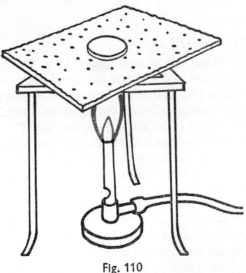

Fig. 110

Experiment 3.16. Place a penny on an asbestos sheet and heat them briefly with a bunsen burner (Fig. 110). Remove the burner and touch the top of the asbestos sheet, then the penny. Can you explain the difference?

If you were to sit on wood, then on concrete, both of which were at the same temperature, which would feel colder? Why?

Heat Conduction in Water

To boil a kettle of water it is necessary to apply heat only to the bottom of the kettle. *As all the water in the kettle reaches boiling point does this suggest that water is a good conductor?* (7) *Explain your answer.* (8)

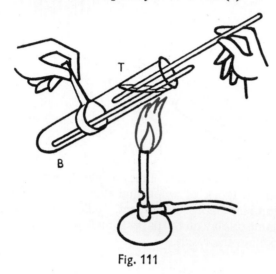

Fig. 111

Experiment 3.17.

(a) Place two thermometers in a test tube full of water and heat it at the top of the tube as shown in Fig. 111. Read both thermometers at regular intervals. When thermometer T reaches 100° C what is the reading on the other?

Repeat the experiment, but this time heat the test tube at the bottom. When thermometer B reaches 100°C what does the other one read?

(b) Alternatively, fix a piece of ice at the bottom of the test tube using a brass nut or piece of wire gauze. Heat the test tube in the middle and see if the ice has melted by the time the water is boiling at the top of the tube.

(c) Here is a simpler qualitative experiment. Hold the bottom end of a boiling tube which contains water and boil the water at the top by heating the tube near the top. Does the water at the bottom become very warm?

Do these experiments suggest that water is a good, or a bad, conductor of heat? Give reasons for your answer.

Heat Conduction in Air

We have seen that when air is heated it rises and carries its heat with it, so that a room can be heated by circulating hot air. Is air, then, a good conductor of heat? To answer this question we must try a few experiments.

Experiment 3.18.

(a) Insert thermometers in two rubber stoppers and fit them at either end of a glass tube

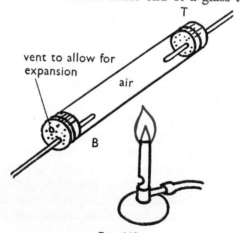

Fig. 112

as shown in Fig. 112. The lower stopper must have a second hole in it to allow air to escape when it expands. With the tube held in the position shown, gently heat the top end and read the temperatures on both thermometers at regular intervals.

Allow the apparatus to cool and then gently heat the lower end of the tube. Read both thermometers at regular intervals as before. Can you explain the results of this experiment? Do they suggest that air is a good or bad conductor of heat?

(b) Hold a finger at either side of a bunsen flame, about half an inch from it. Does the result suggest that air is a good conductor of heat?

Experiment 3.19. Take two identical cans or calorimeters and pour equal volumes of hot water at the same temperature into each. Put a thermometer into each calorimeter and place a card over the top to reduce heat loss by convection. Both calorimeters should be placed on corks, one standing on a bench and the other in a container loosely packed with cotton wool. Air is trapped between the fibres of the cotton wool so that convection currents are reduced.

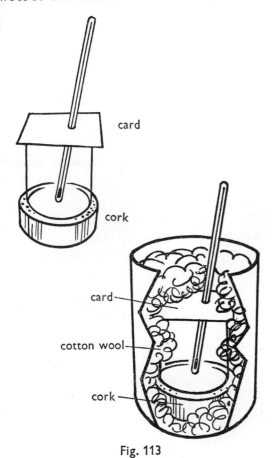

card

cork

card

cotton wool

cork

Fig. 113

Compare the temperatures in the two calorimeters at regular intervals. Does your result suggest that cotton wool is a good or a bad thermal (heat) conductor? As the cotton wool is full of trapped air, what does this suggest?

Normally heat is carried in air by convection currents. If the air is trapped, however, so that such currents cannot flow, much less heat is transmitted. It is for this reason that wool, fur and feathers keep animals, and us, warm. *Why do string vests (a series of holes tied together) keep you warm? (9)* Water pipes are lagged with felt, and walls and ceilings are sometimes lined with glass fibre to reduce heat loss. In both of those materials air is trapped, thus making them good thermal insulators. *Why can a snow-built igloo keep Eskimos warm? (10)*

Thermal Conduction

The experiments we have been doing show us that metals conduct heat and electricity very well. Some other solids conduct heat, but not so readily as metals. We have also seen that water and air are poor conductors of heat. This is true of most liquids and gases.

Infra-red radiation

There is nothing between the sun and the Earth to conduct heat or to allow convection currents to flow, yet we are warmed by the sun's rays. There must be another way in which heat can be transmitted from one place to another.

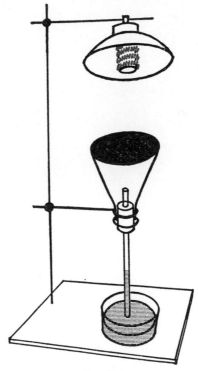

Fig. 114

Demonstration 3.20. Construct a simple thermoscope and paint the base of the flask matt black. Hold your hands round the flask so that some air is expelled and then allow it to cool when some of the coloured water will be pushed up the tube. What pushes the water up the tube? Fix an electric radiator above the thermoscope and switch it on. Watch the water in the tube. What does its movement indicate? Has heat travelled by conduction or convection?

With a variable transformer, gradually reduce the voltage applied to the electric radiator until it just ceases to glow red. Switch off the radiator now and allow the air in the thermoscope to cool down. Finally switch on the radiator so that it does not glow and see if heat is being transmitted to the thermoscope. Such radiation is called infra-red radiation.

Infra-red radiation reaches us from the sun through empty space. It is sometimes referred to as thermal radiation or radiant 'heat'. Much of the heat from red-hot sources, such as coal, gas and electric fires is transmitted as infra-red radiation.

We will be dealing with waves more fully in the next section and will continue our study of this type of radiation then.

Visual aids

Charts

Science for Today. No. 3. Keeping Ourselves Warm$_{36}$.

16 mm Sound Films

DCF 2664 Convection of Heat$_{52}$
DCF 2665 Conduction of Heat$_{52}$
DCF 2666 Radiation of Heat$_{52}$
20.7222 Heat: Its nature and transfer$_{44}$

Waves

CHAPTER 4

Transverse waves

In the last section we considered the flow of particles such as electrons and molecules. We now ask the question, 'Can anything other than a particle, or stream of particles, move from one point to another?' In this section we will deal with the transmission of *energy* by various types of wave motion.

Travelling Pulses

If a rope or coil spring is tied to a tree, and the free end is held as shown in Fig. 115, a pulse

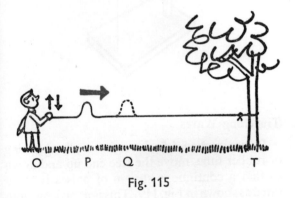

Fig. 115

can be transmitted along the rope by moving the free end up and down. The movement causing the pulse is the up-and-down jerk at O. The pulse, or disturbance, moves from O to P and then to Q and so on until it reaches the tree T. Notice carefully that (a) the pulse moves along the rope at a fairly constant speed, (b) the rope moves at right angles to the motion of the pulse, and (c) the pulse is *caused* by moving particles—the rope's movement at O—but the pulse itself is not *composed* of particles moving from O to T. The pulse carries *energy* from O to T.

You should study the behaviour of moving pulses in at least one of the following demonstrations.

Demonstration 4.1.

(a) Fill a long length of rubber tubing with sand, and attach one end to a nail in the wall. The sand reduces the speed at which the pulses travel and enables you to observe them more easily. Alternatively you may use heavy pressure tubing. Holding the tubing horizontally, give the free end a sharp up-and-down jerk as shown in Fig. 115, and watch the moving pulse. What happens when the pulse reaches the nail? If the original pulse curved upwards above the general level of the tubing as shown in Fig. 115, what can you say about the reflected pulse? What happens to the size (amplitude) of the pulse as it moves along?

opposite side of tube, smaller

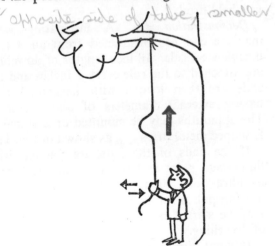

Fig. 116

(b) If your laboratory has a very high ceiling the rubber tubing can be hung vertically as shown in Fig. 116. The pulses can often be seen more easily with a rope suspended in this way.

Demonstration 4.2.

(*a*) Attach a long coil spring₄ to a nail in the wall and pull it horizontally until it is slightly stretched. Transmit a pulse along the spring and observe its behaviour.

(*b*) Lay a slinky₄ or the above coil spring on *opposite side* a smooth floor and hold one end of the spring. Study the movement of a pulse sent along the spring from the free end.

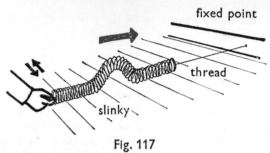

fixed point

thread

slinky

Fig. 117

Demonstration 4.3. Stretch a slinky along a smooth floor and attach a long fine thread to one end (Fig. 117). Give the free end of the slinky a sharp sideways jerk so that a pulse runs along the slinky. When the pulse reaches the thread, is it reflected or transmitted along the thread? How does this differ from the result obtained when one end of the slinky was held firmly?

reflected, but some energy moves down the thread. Comes back same side.

Demonstration 4.4. A fascinating wave machine can be constructed from an 8 foot flexible steel rule. 18 inch lengths of dowelling are attached to the rule every 3 inches and the ends are then loaded with hexagonal nuts having external diameters of about 1 inch. The apparatus may be mounted on a frame of L-shaped metal strips ₃₁,₃₂ as shown in Fig. 118.

If the ends of the nuts are painted with fluorescent paint and the apparatus is viewed in ultra-violet light, the behaviour of slow moving pulses can be studied clearly. A pulse may be started by displacing the lowest strip of dowelling.

In what direction do the nuts move? Does the pulse move in the same direction? What happens to the wave when it is reflected from a fixed end?

Wave machines of this type are available commercially₂₆.

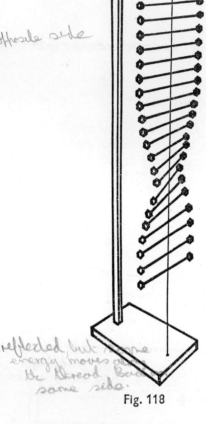

Fig. 118

Travelling Waves

Demonstration 4.5. Using a very long spring or rubber tube, move the free end up and down so that a continuous stream of pulses is generated as shown in Fig. 119. This is a wave motion. Waves travel along the tube in the direction

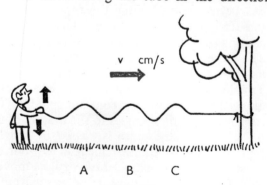

v cm/s

A   B   C

Fig. 119

of the arrow. We will assume that the speed (or velocity) at which the waves travel along the tube is v cm/s. As the tube is long we can consider what happens *before* the disturbance reaches the fixed end and is reflected.

The original crest formed at A gradually moves to B. By this time a new crest has formed at A. Those two crests now move to B and C, by which time a third crest has formed at A. The regions between the crests are referred to as *troughs*.

Are there any particles moving along in the direction shown by the red arrow? What *is* moving in that direction? If a microscopically small dwarf were sitting on the middle of the tube in what direction would he move? Would he move at a steady speed of v cm/s?

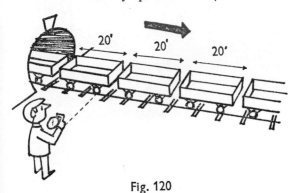

Fig. 120

Suppose you are standing at the end of a tunnel from which a long goods train is emerging. You know that each truck is 20 feet long and you count the number of trucks passing you in, say, 10 seconds. This enables you to find the number of trucks passing you every second, that is, the *frequency* (f) at which trucks pass you. If 20 trucks pass in 10 seconds then, on the average, $\frac{20}{10} = 2$ trucks pass every second. We can therefore say that the frequency (f) = 2 trucks per second. Can you calculate the velocity of the train?

As each truck is 20 feet long and 2 trucks pass every second, the train must go 20×2 feet in 1 second. Its velocity is therefore 40 ft/s.

velocity = truck length × number of trucks passing per second

that is, velocity = truck length × frequency

Let us represent the length of the truck by the Greek letter l. It is called lambda and looks like the letter y upside down: λ.

We can now write the speed or velocity of the goods train as

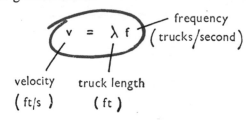

Let us now return to the waves travelling along a rope. At any instant the distance between two adjacent crests or troughs is called the wavelength, and we will again use the Greek letter λ to indicate this length.

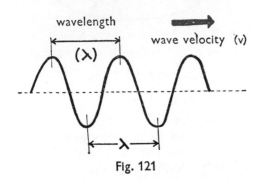

Fig. 121

The speed at which any particular crest or trough moves along the rope is called the *wave velocity* (v).

The number of complete jerks or *cycles* every second is called the *frequency* (f). If the operator moves the rope up and down twice every second we say that the frequency is two cycles per second (2 c/s or 2 c.p.s.).

Imagine now that waves of wavelength (λ) = 200 cm are being sent along a very long rope (Fig. 122). An observer standing at the side of the rope finds how many crests are passing every second, that is, he finds the frequency. The observer discovers that the frequency is 2 c/s. Can he calculate the wave velocity?

As each wave is 200 cm long and 2 waves pass every second the wave must travel at 200×2 cm every second.

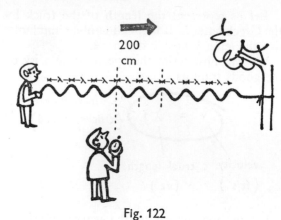

200
cm

Fig. 122

Wave velocity = wavelength × number of waves per second

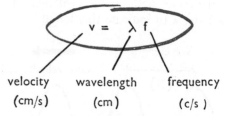

$$v = \lambda f$$

velocity   wavelength   frequency
(cm/s)   (cm)   (c/s)

Wave Machines

Demonstration 4.6. In transverse waves the particles move at right angles to the direction in which the wave moves. This can be demonstrated very simply with the Russian wave machine (Fig. 123)[18].

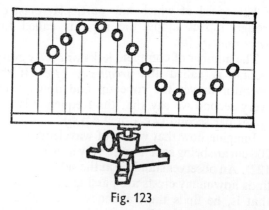

Fig. 123

White beads representing the particles move vertically on wires. By moving these beads in a particular way a wave can be seen to move *horizontally* along the board although the beads themselves move only *vertically*.

Demonstration 4.7.

(*a*) Wind an open coil spring with heavy wire and pivot it as shown in Fig. 124. If a car headlamp bulb is used to cast a shadow of the spring on a screen, a travelling wave can be seen when the coil is rotated. Do particles of the spring move along when the spring is rotated?

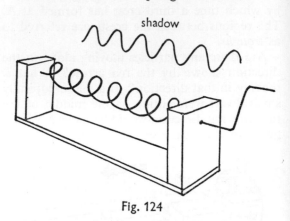

shadow

Fig. 124

(*b*) A similar demonstration can be produced using a number of beads attached to wires as shown in Fig. 125.

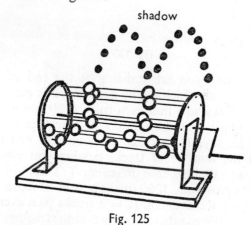

shadow

Fig. 125

What Happens When Waves Meet?

From the following experiment you should try to find out what happens to two waves or pulses when they move in opposite directions along a spring or rope.

Experiment 4.8. Place a long coil spring or slinky on a smooth floor and stretch it slightly. The spring should be held by a pupil at each end. A pulse should then be sent along the spring from each end at the same instant. Try this experiment with the jerks in (*a*) the same direction and (*b*) opposite directions. Can you adjust the pulses so that the centre of the coil remains undisturbed? When does this occur? What happens to the pulses when they meet? Do they pass each other and continue as if nothing had happened?

Reflections and Standing Waves

You have already discovered that waves in a spring are reflected when the spring is held tightly or loosely at the end. *In what way does the reflected wave differ in those two cases? (1)* Remember that when a spring exerts a force on (say) a wall the wall exerts a force on the spring. *What can you say about the directions of these two forces? (2)*

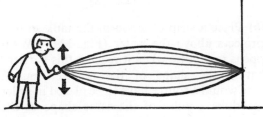

Fig. 126

Experiment 4.9. Tie one end of a spring or a piece of rubber tubing to a wall and send waves along it. Now gradually alter the frequency at which you transmit the waves, until the reflected wave combines with the transmitted wave so that the travelling wave disappears and the spring now vibrates up and down. You have now produced a *standing wave*. How can you produce standing waves of the type shown in Fig. 126 at higher frequencies?

Demonstration 4.10.

(*a*) Tie a piece of elastic thread, about 2 metres long, to a vibration generator$_{27}$. Secure the other end of the elastic to a retort stand. Wire the generator to an audio oscillator such as the Advance J1 which has a low impedance output.

Increase the frequency of the oscillator from

its minimum setting until a standing wave of the type shown in Fig. 126 is produced. Note the oscillator frequency. Continue increasing the frequency until another standing wave is set up. What is the oscillator frequency now? How is the frequency related to the original (fundamental) frequency?

If the elastic is coated with white chalk it is interesting to view it with a stroboscope lamp.

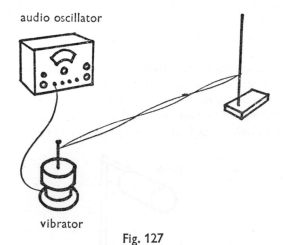

audio oscillator

vibrator

Fig. 127

(*b*) A simple alternative experiment can be conducted using an electric bell or ticker-tape vibrator with a light string or thread hung from the clapper. Standing waves can be set up in the thread by holding the lower end and varying the tension.

Travelling Waves and Standing Waves

Travelling waves *transmit energy* from one place (the source) to another. Sea waves transmit enough energy to destroy sea walls, and sound waves from an explosion can shatter windows. Standing waves, on the other hand, *store energy* in vibrations. The energy stored in the standing waves in a vibrating string may, however, be used to produce (travelling) sound waves. We will be dealing with such waves more fully in the next chapter.

Water waves

A pulse travels along a horizontal rope because one part of the rope as it moves upwards (say) pulls the next part of the rope up and in so doing loses some, and ultimately all, of its own motion. Thus the up-and-down motion (energy) is transmitted horizontally along the rope at the wave velocity. Remember that the horizontal wave velocity does not depend on the velocity of the rope particles which move up and down at quite different speeds.

Water waves have many similar properties to waves produced in ropes and springs. In each case energy is transmitted by a vibrating material. We can study water waves most easily in a ripple tank such as the P.S.S.C. type of tank[2,4,16].

Water waves are transmitted over the water surface. *If you were a submarine commander and your submarine was afloat on a stormy sea what would you do and why? (3) What happens to a floating cork as a wave passes by? (4)*

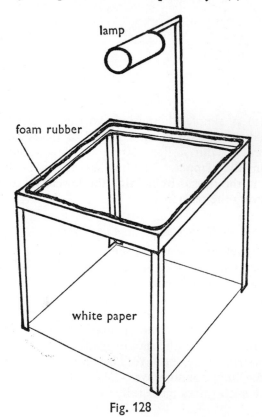

Fig. 128

Reflection

Experiment 4.11.

(a) Set up the ripple tank as shown in Fig. 128. A 12 volt car bulb is a suitable source of light. Pour water into the tank and adjust the feet until the depth is about half an inch at all four corners. When the water is calm touch the centre of the water surface with the point of a pencil or allow a drop of water to fall from a small pipette. What is the shape of the pulse obtained? What does this tell you about the speed at which the pulse moves in all directions?

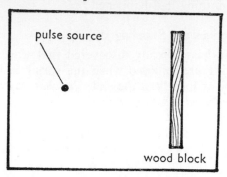

Fig. 129

(b) Place a strip of wood in the tank so that it projects above the water (Fig. 129). What happens to a pulse when it reaches this barrier? What is the shape of the reflected pulse? Where would a source have to be placed in order to produce a pulse of the same shape as the *reflected* pulse? Such a source is called a *virtual source*. The reflected pulse behaves *as if* it came from this virtual source.

(c) Repeat the two experiments above, using a point source vibrator to produce a series of pulses or waves. The wave pattern produced on the screen can be more easily studied if you observe it through a hand stroboscope[4]. Alternatively the ripple tank can be illuminated by a stroboscope lamp or by an ordinary lamp shining through a rotating disc in which holes have been cut.

Experiment 4.12.

(a) Produce a straight pulse by rolling, in a forward-and-backward jerk, a length of half inch dowelling or glass tube as shown in Fig. 130. Allow the pulse to strike a strip of wood placed parallel to the oncoming pulse (position A). How is the pulse reflected? Now rotate the wood to position B and again study the direction of a reflected pulse.

Repeat this experiment with the wood strip lying at different angles. See if you can find how to *predict* the direction of the reflected pulse. It may help you to do this if you place a piece of paper under the ripple tank, and draw on it the reflecting surface and the directions in which the original and reflected pulses are moving.

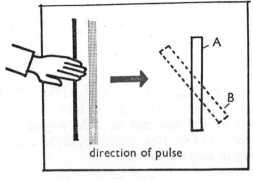

direction of pulse

Fig. 130

(*b*) Repeat the above experiments using a plane wave generator, and use a stroboscope to examine the patterns produced. Do the waves move in straight lines or do they bend? Do you think the reflected waves have the same frequency, wave length and velocity as the incident waves?

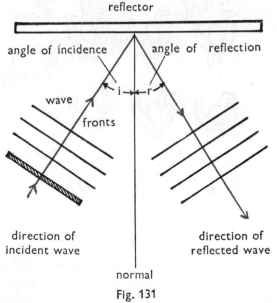

Fig. 131

Wave front and wave direction

Do not confuse the wave front with the direction in which it moves. The wave moves at right angles to the wave front. It is usual to measure the angle between the wave direction and a line drawn at right angles to the reflecting surface. This line is called the *normal*.

The angle between the direction of the incident wave and the normal is referred to as the *angle of incidence*, and the angle between the direction of the reflected wave and the normal is called the *angle of reflection*. From the last experiment how do you think those angles are related? (5)

Refraction

Wave velocity

If you know the wavelength (λ) and the frequency (f) of a wave how can you calculate its velocity? (6) In the following experiment you should use this relationship to find the velocity of the water waves in a ripple tank.

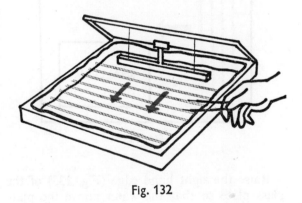

Fig. 132

Experiment 4.13. Set up a plane wave generator, operated by an electric motor, in the ripple tank and illuminate it with a flashing source of light. Starting with a high frequency gradually reduce the frequency of the light flashes, until you find the highest frequency at which the motor spindle appears stationary without 'double viewing'. Use a pair of dividers as shown in Fig. 132 to find the wavelength of the water waves.

Now find the frequency of vibration of the plane wave generator. Having found the wavelength and the frequency you should calculate the wave velocity.

What happens to the wavelength of the waves when the vibrator frequency is increased?

You can use a hand stroboscope if a flashing light source is not available.

Experiment 4.14. In this experiment you should try to discover if water waves travel at different speeds in deep and shallow water. Place a quarter-inch thick glass plate in the ripple tank so that a very shallow layer of water lies on top of it. In the rest of the ripple tank the water will be much deeper. Use (*a*) a single pulse and (*b*) a plane wave generator to send waves along the tank and see if their speed changes when they reach the shallow water. What conclusion do you reach?

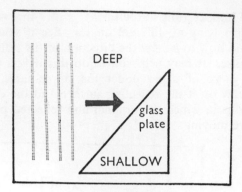

Fig. 134

Imagine that a platoon is given the following orders. The men are to march in files of three so that the files are at right angles to the direction of motion. Secondly, the men have to keep in step all the time.

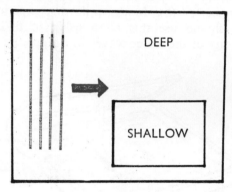

Fig. 133

Raise the right hand edge (Fig. 133) of the glass plate so that the water above the plate becomes shallower and shallower. How does this affect the wavelength and speed of the waves? What would you expect to happen to the speed of sea waves as they come towards the shore?

Experiment 4.15. Repeat the last experiment, using a triangular glass plate. Part of the wave will be slowed down as it reaches the shallow water. What happens to the direction of the waves when they are slowed down? Do the waves in the shallow water move in a straight line?

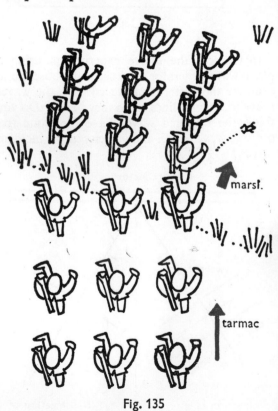

Fig. 135

The column starts off on a tarmac road and then obliquely approaches a marshy piece of ground (Fig. 135). In the marsh the going is more difficult and the men will move more slowly, but as they have to keep step with the others (i.e. the *frequency* of the footsteps must remain the same) they must take shorter steps (i.e. their *step-length* is smaller). The men in the right hand rank will be slowed down first and the file will wheel to the right. The direction of the column will therefore change when the men cross the boundary between the tarmac and the marsh.

You might like to try this out in the playground, using (say) grass in place of the marsh.

When waves pass at an angle from one substance to another in which their speed is different, they are bent so that they move off in a different direction. This bending of waves at a boundary is called *refraction*. The greater the change of speed, the greater is the amount of bending that occurs.

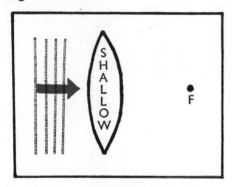

Fig. 136

Experiment 4.16. Place a lens-shaped piece of plate glass or quarter inch perspex in the ripple tank and send plane waves towards it as shown in Fig. 136. Observe the bending that takes place when the waves are slowed down as they pass over the 'lens'. Draw a diagram of the pattern produced and state what you think point F represents in Fig. 136.

Diffraction

Experiment 4.17.

(a) Send plane waves along the ripple tank using the plane wave generator. Now place two blocks of wood or glass in the path of the waves so that a 10 centimetre opening is left in the middle to allow the waves to pass. Examine the shape of the waves which pass through the opening. Gradually reduce the width of the gap between the blocks and note any change that takes place in the shape of the waves passing through the gap. What is the shape of the waves which have passed through a gap smaller than the wavelength of the water waves?

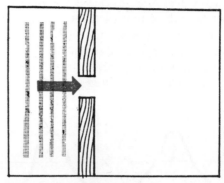

Fig. 137

Alter the frequency of the source so that the wavelength is altered. The size of the gap should be kept constant. Which waves are bent more, the long or the short waves?

(b) Replace the blocks of wood by a piece of ¼ in brass rod about 1 in long set vertically in the water. Now send plane waves along the ripple tank and see if the rod casts a 'shadow'. Try placing various objects of different sizes in the path of the waves, and say what effects are produced by objects smaller than the wavelengths of the water waves.

The last experiments show that when plane waves pass through a small opening or round a small object they are bent. They emerge from the opening as almost circular waves and they bend round the small object and continue as if the object were not there at all. This kind of bending of waves is called *diffraction*.

Interference

Billiard balls will bounce off a cushion so that the angle of incidence is equal to the angle of reflection. They are not waves. Men marching in files can be made to change direction when they move over a surface on which their speed is altered, and they are certainly not waves. A stream of particles can be bent by gravitational, magnetic, electric and other forces. Again, they are not waves.

Is there then any property of waves which does not apply to anything else? Is there any clue which shows us that we are dealing with waves?

If two waves are produced on the surface of a ripple tank so that two crests appear at the same place at the same time (P and Q, Fig. 138(a)), the result will be similar to that shown at R. The crests add together to form a bigger crest. They are said to be *in phase*.

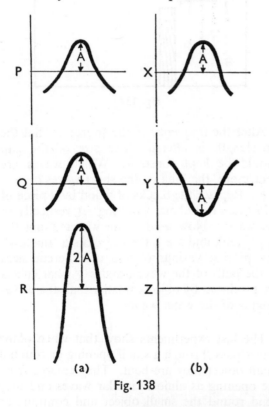

(a)   (b)

Fig. 138

If, however, the crests are as shown in Fig. 138(b), the crest of X comes at the same place and time as a trough of Y and they cancel each other. In this case they are said to be exactly *out of phase* with each other. The crests X and Y therefore add up to Z, which is zero!

Here then is a certain test for waves. Waves can combine (or *interfere*) in such a way that they either produce a larger wave or a smaller wave. If the waves are identical, they will produce crests of double the original size where they are in phase, and they will cancel each other where they are exactly out of phase.

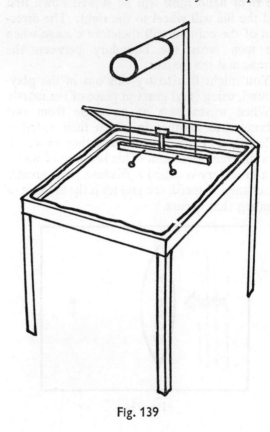

Fig. 139

Experiment 4.18.

(a) Using the wave generator fitted with two point sources placed about 5 to 10 centimetres apart, produce two sets of circular waves. As the waves are produced by the same vibrating bar they will have the same frequency. Study the pattern produced as the frequency of vibration is altered. Can you detect what occurs when (a) two crests meet and (b) a crest and a trough meet? You will see the effect more clearly if you use a stroboscope.

(b) Similar interference patterns may be produced by sending plane waves through a double slit. The apparatus should be set up as in Experiment 4.17(a) and an additional wooden block used to form two small gaps about 5 centimetres apart.

Interference Patterns

The circles in Fig. 140 represent wave crests. They produce light bands when they meet, thus representing additive interference. Dark bands representing destructive interference are produced when crests and troughs meet. If you half close your eyes you can see these bands in Fig. 140.

Fig. 140

We may have to try to find out if a certain effect is produced by waves. Often we cannot see whether there are waves of any kind, and in such cases we will look for *interference patterns*. If they can be found we can safely assume that we are dealing with something which has a wave nature.

Sound Interference

Experiment 4.19. Fix an earphone in a wooden cap into which two brass tubes have been inserted. Connect the brass tubes to a similar cap, using a 7 foot and a 9 foot length of rubber tubing. As in the case of the ripple tank a single vibrator produces, in effect, two sources. Feed a sound signal into the earphone and listen to the note at the far end of the tubes.

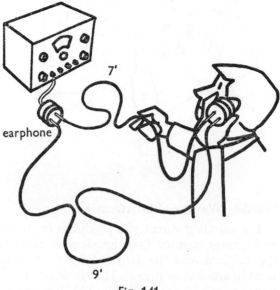

Fig. 141

Alter the frequency of the sound by varying the oscillator frequency until minimum volume is heard. For the lengths given, minima should occur at about 270 c/s and 800 c/s. If you have adjusted the frequency correctly, the volume of the note should *increase* when either tube is pinched. Why is this? What does this tell you about sound?

Light Interference

Experiment 4.20. Paint a glass slide with $Aquadag_{18}$ and use two razor blades to mark two thin parallel lines across it. Make the lines as close to each other as possible. Place another slide on top of the painted surface to protect it and bind the slides together with adhesive tape. View a show case lamp (60 watt, clear glass, tubular, double ended) through the slits, holding the slide so that the slits are parallel to the lamp filament, (Fig. 142). The two slits, side by side, then act as two sources of the same frequency, as did the point sources in the ripple tank experiment.

Why are there bands of light and darkness? What does this tell you?

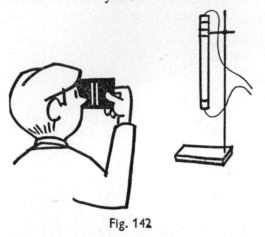

Fig. 142

Standing Waves and Interference

The standing waves you produced in strings and springs resulted from interference between the original and the reflected waves as they went in and out of phase. The resultant of two such waves is illustrated in Fig. 143. The graphs on the right show how the two waves may be added together.

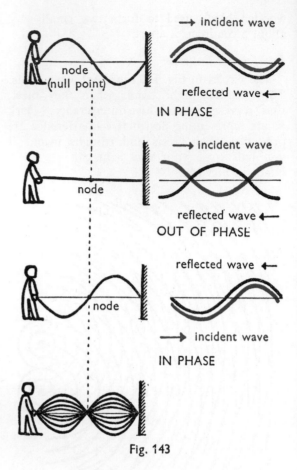

Fig. 143

Visual aids

8 mm Cassettes

PM/014 Transverse Waves[41]
PM/060 Longitudinal Waves[41]
PM/024 Ripple Tank Experiments: Refraction[41]
Ripple Tank Wave Phenomena Nos. 1, 2, 4, 5 and 6[43]

PM/359 Diffraction at an Aperture[40]
GL/1 Two Sources in Phase[40]

16 mm Sound Films

Common Wave Behaviour[42]
21.7485 Waves and Energy[41]
D 2571 Simple Waves[52]

Sound waves

CHAPTER 5

Longitudinal waves

In our experiments with springs and with water, we have seen waves produced by particles vibrating at right angles to the direction in which the wave was travelling. Such waves are called *transverse waves*. It is, however, possible for particles to vibrate in the same direction as that in which the wave is travelling.

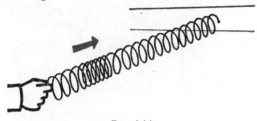

Fig. 144

Experiment 5.1.

(*a*) Stretch a long slinky on a smooth bench or floor and hold one end stationary. Now give the free end a sharp push so that the spring is compressed at that end. A compression pulse will run along the spring. What happens when the pulse reaches the fixed end?

(*b*) Move the free end of the spring backwards and forwards so that it is alternately compressed and stretched. What do you observe? Are the coils of the spring moving at right angles to the direction in which the wave is travelling or in the same direction?

Where the spring is stretched we say *rarefaction* occurs and where the coils are squeezed together *compression* takes place.

Suppose a dwarf were sitting on the slinky at D; how would he move? (1) Would the direction in which he moved always be parallel to the wave motion? (2) Waves of this kind are called compression waves or *longitudinal waves*.

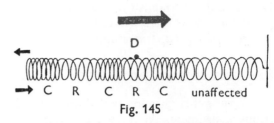

Fig. 145

Demonstration 5.2. Use the Russian wave machine to demonstrate longitudinal travelling waves produced by particles vibrating backwards and forwards.

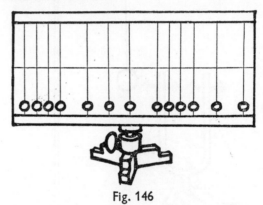

Fig. 146

Longitudinal waves have many similar properties to transverse waves. For example, they transmit energy in a given medium at a particular velocity. The number of compressions produced per second is called the frequency and the distance between successive compressions is the wavelength. As with transverse waves the velocity may be found by multiplying the wavelength and the frequency.

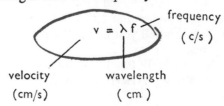

$$v = \lambda f$$

velocity (cm/s)   wavelength (cm)   frequency (c/s)

Noises and notes

Energy is always required to produce sound waves. The kinetic energy of a brick hurled through a window will produce a *noise*. A guitar string will produce a *note* if it is plucked. *How would you distinguish between a noise and a note?* (3) This chapter is mainly concerned with the study of sounds which are produced by regular vibrations. We will consider how such notes are produced, transmitted and detected.

How are sounds produced?

To answer this question you should examine various instruments to see what they have in common when they produce sounds.

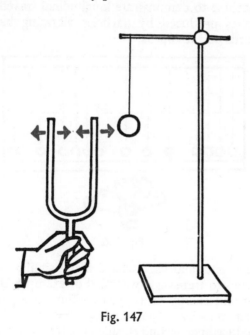

Fig. 147

Experiment 5.3.

(*a*) Bring a tuning fork which is producing a note up to a suspended pith ball until one of the prongs touches the ball. What happens? What does this tell you about the prong of the tuning fork?

(*b*) Alternatively touch a calm water surface with the tuning fork prong and explain the result.

Experiment 5.4. Place the base of a vibrating tuning fork on a bench. Do you think the vibrations are transmitted to the bench? Why is there a difference in the loudness of the note? You can mystify your friends by pretending to collect the sound with your left hand from above the fork and directing it into a tumbler when the amplitude will suddenly increase. The illusion is produced by secretly allowing the base of the tuning fork to touch the table as your left hand reaches the tumbler (Fig. 148).

Fig. 148

Experiment 5.5. Connect an old loudspeaker to a radio set, amplifier or oscillator so that it produces various sounds. Place the speaker horizontally and lay a few plastic beads in the cone. How does the distance the cone moves (amplitude) alter as the volume of sound is increased? Touch the cone lightly and describe the sensation. Now examine the moving cone illuminated by a stroboscope lamp.

When the cone of a loudspeaker moves forwards (Fig. 149), the air in front of it is compressed; when it moves backwards the air in front is rarefied. If the cone vibrates continuously, successive regions of compressed and rarefied air are formed. The compressions and rarefactions move outwards from the source at the speed of sound but the air itself does *not* move outwards. Compare this behaviour with the water waves produced in a ripple tank or the compression waves produced in a slinky. *Did the water move away from the rippler? (4) Did the first few turns of the slinky move along the coil? (5)*

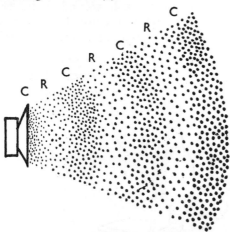

Fig. 149

If you turn on a gas tap for a few seconds, someone, a few feet away, will hear the escaping gas long before he smells it. The sound is certainly not being carried by gas molecules moving from the tap to the hearer otherwise he would hear and smell the gas at the same time.

represented by an arrow the length of which indicates how far the molecule has moved from its original position. The direction of the arrow shows which way the molecule has moved (c). By rotating these arrows through 90° we can construct a graph which represents the displacement of the air molecules (d). Note that although the graph goes *up and down* it represents the movement of particles which vibrate *backwards and forwards*. A graph of this shape can be used to represent transverse or longitudinal waves.

Experiment 5.6.

(a) Examine various percussion instruments such as cymbals, drums, bells, triangles or xylophones. What happens if the sounding instrument is touched? Why?

(b) Pluck a violin or guitar string. Why does the note disappear if the string is touched? Depress the sustaining pedal on a piano and press a key. What happens when you release the pedal? Why?

(c) Try to build a simple xylophone from different lengths of *hard* wood.

In all the above cases sounds were produced when solids such as metals, skins, strings and

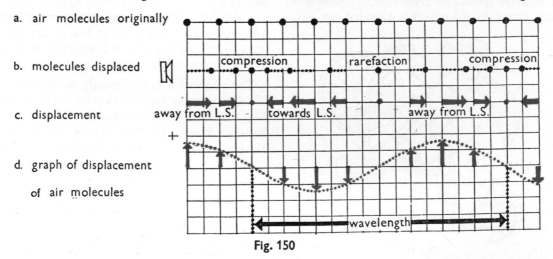

a. air molecules originally

b. molecules displaced

c. displacement

d. graph of displacement
   of air molecules

Fig. 150

Fig. 150(a) represents undisturbed air molecules. A vibrating loudspeaker cone displaces the molecules to form regions of compression and rarefaction (b). The displacement of each molecule at one particular instant of time is

paper vibrated to and fro. The energy was then transmitted by longitudinal waves. *Can you think of an example of sounds being produced by a moving liquid? (6)* In general sounds are not produced by vibrating liquids, although

Fig. 151

sound waves can travel through liquids very easily. We will consider the case of vibrating gases, such as air, after we have discussed *resonance*.

Pitch and frequency

Experiment 5.7. Turn a bicycle upside down and spin the back wheel. Hold a piece of card on the tyre tread and report on any change in pitch heard as the wheel is speeded up. Can

Fig. 152

you find out how many times per second the card is vibrating when you turn the pedals at a steady rate? Describe how you did this and state the answer you obtained. What is the 'number of vibrations per second' called?

Demonstration 5.8. Blow air from a vacuum cleaner or foot bellows through a series of holes in a disc as shown in Fig. 153. As the disc is speeded up, the number of blasts of air passing through the holes each second is increased. How does the pitch of the note heard vary with the frequency of air blasts? Some commercially

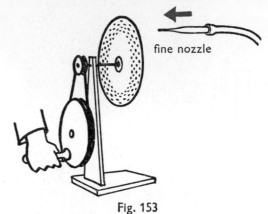

fine nozzle

Fig. 153

produced sirens are fitted with revolution counters which enable you to count the number of blasts in several seconds, and hence to calculate the frequency. Why should you not read the number of blasts of air during only one second?

If the disc has several concentric sets of holes which will produce 24, 30, 36 and 48 blasts per revolution, you can play a tune from the notes doh, me, soh, doh'.

The pitch of a note depends on the number of vibrations per second, that is, the frequency. For scientific purposes middle C is taken as 256 c/s, whilst the note an octave lower is 128 c/s and the note an octave above middle C is 512 c/s.

Note	doh	me	soh	doh'
No. of air blasts per second	24	30	36	48
f = fundamental	f	$\frac{5}{4}f$	$\frac{3}{2}f$	$2f$
doh = middle C	256	$\frac{5}{4}.256$	$\frac{3}{2}.256$	2.256
	256	320	384	512

Vibrations that we can hear are said to be *audible*, and the frequencies of such vibrations are called *audio* frequencies. *Does this mean that there are sounds we cannot hear?* (7) Dogs can certainly hear high pitched whistles to which we are deaf, and bats produce sounds which they can hear although we cannot. Frequencies too high for us to hear are called *ultrasonic* frequencies.

Fig. 154

The range of frequencies which can be heard varies from person to person, and as we grow older this range becomes gradually less and less. The normal range of a young person may be between 20 cycles per second and 20,000 cycles per second. It is claimed that many HiFi tape and disc reproducers cover this frequency range. It is necessary, however, to have a very good system of loudspeakers if such a range is to be reproduced adequately. You will be able to get some idea of the frequencies you can hear from the following demonstration.

Demonstration 5.9. Connect an audio oscillator, such as the $J1_{27}$ or $A050/T_{34}$, to a good loudspeaker system. Vary the frequency of the oscillator over the audio range and discover the highest and lowest notes which you can detect.

Resonance

Demonstration 5.10. Stretch a piece of string between two retort stands or across a wire frame as shown in Fig. 155. Attach to the

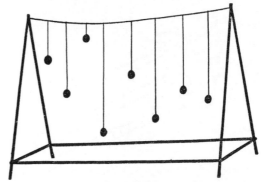

Fig. 155

string a number of pendulums of various lengths making two of them equal. Set one of the two identical pendulums swinging and watch its effect on the others. What do you observe?

Experiment 5.11. You can follow Christopher Robin's example by having 'fun in the bath tonight'. Move your body to produce a

Fig. 156

wave which is sent along the bath and then reflected. If you send the reflected wave back again by pushing the water at the right time you can build up a very respectable wave.

Warning: mop up the bathroom before you leave!

Experiment 5.12. Fix three hacksaw blades to a piece of wood as shown in Fig. 157. Suitable lengths are 14 inches, 12 inches and 10 inches. The longer lengths may be obtained by soldering two pieces together if necessary.

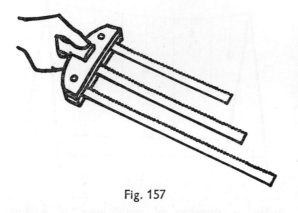

Fig. 157

Shake the apparatus so that the longest strip vibrates most violently. Now try to make the centre strip and then the shortest strip vibrate in turn, with maximum amplitude. The frequency at which the greatest amplitude of vibration is obtained for each strip is called the natural or *resonant frequency* of the strip. How does the resonant frequency vary with the length of the strip?

It is often possible to tell the approximate speed of a car or a bus by the rattles! At different speeds different parts of the car start to vibrate. Each has its own natural vibration time

A children's swing has its own natural frequency. To obtain the maximum amplitude with the minimum effort, energy has to be fed into it (that is, it has to be pushed) at this frequency. Even large structures such as suspension bridges have resonant frequencies. Soldiers marching in step over such a bridge can set it into vibration at this frequency. The vibrations build up so that the bridge may eventually collapse. There are at least two recorded instances of bridges collapsing as a result of soldiers marching across them. One was near Manchester (1831) and the other across the River Maine in France (1849).

What precaution is now taken to prevent such disasters? (8)

In 1940 a suspension bridge across the Tacoma Narrows in America collapsed owing to gusts of wind setting it swinging at its resonant frequency.

Vibrating Strings

In the last chapter we considered standing waves produced in strings, springs and ropes. Those waves were seen to result from interference between the incident and the reflected wave as they went in and out of phase. Stringed instruments produce musical notes because of such standing waves set up at the *resonant frequencies* of the strings. You can study these waves in the following demonstration.

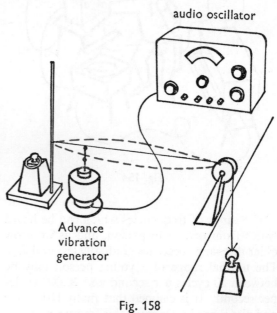

audio oscillator

Advance vibration generator

Fig. 158

Demonstration 5.13.

(*a*) Attach a light string about two metres long to a heavy retort stand as shown in Fig. 158. The string should pass over a pulley and have a mass of about 200 grams attached to it to keep it under tension. Tie a piece of elastic to the string about 10 centimetres from the retort stand, and attach the other end of the elastic to an Advance vibration generator which should be powered by an audio oscillator. If you want an audible indication of the frequency being used connect a loudspeaker across the generator terminals.

Adjust the frequency of the oscillator until the string vibrates with a single loop as indicated in red in Fig. 158. Note the oscillator frequency. This is called the *fundamental frequency* of the string.

Now increase the frequency of oscillation until two loops are formed, and again note the frequency. How does it compare with the fundamental frequency? This new frequency is called the *second harmonic*. Can you find the third and fourth harmonics? Fascinating results may be obtained by illuminating the vibrating string with a strobe lamp.

(*b*) Using the same apparatus as above, increase the tension in the string by adding extra masses to the end. Find the new fundamental frequency for the string. How does it compare with the original?

(*c*) Keeping the tension in the string constant, reduce the length and again find the fundamental frequency. How has shortening the string affected its resonant frequency?

The frequency at which a string vibrates depends on its length and tension.

The frequency increases as the tension increases.
The frequency decreases as the length increases.

How does a guitarist adjust the frequency at which a string vibrates (a) when he is tuning the guitar and (b) when he is playing it? (9) How do the strings which produce the low notes on a piano differ from those which produce the high notes? (10)

Air Vibrations

We have seen that musical notes can be produced by solid objects such as forks, bells and strings as they vibrate at their natural frequencies. In the following experiments we will attempt to produce notes by causing air to vibrate in various tubes.

Demonstration 5.14.

(*a*) Fit a piston to a length of glass tubing about a foot long and half an inch in diameter. Blow across the end of the tube until a note is

Fig. 159

heard (Fig. 159). Now alter the position of the piston and try again. How does the pitch of the note alter as the length of the air column is increased?

(*b*) Alternatively use a number of test tubes containing different volumes of water.

Experiment 5.15. Squeeze the end of a drinking straw so that about an inch is flattened. Trim the corners with scissors (Fig. 160(*a*)). Place the trimmed end in your mouth and try to produce a steady note by blowing.

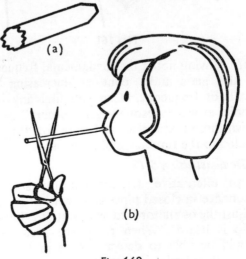

Fig. 160

Now cut an inch off the end of the straw (Fig. 160(*b*)) and explain why the pitch of the note has altered. Continue shortening the straw bit by bit.

Demonstration 5.16.

(*a*) Attach a small cardboard piston to the Advance vibration generator and place it near one end of a glass tube as shown in Fig. 161. Using an audio oscillator to feed the generator, gradually increase the frequency until the note heard suddenly becomes louder. This is due to a standing wave having been produced in the tube. Sound waves must therefore have been reflected at the open end of the tube thus setting up standing waves. The lowest resonant frequency is again called the fundamental frequency.

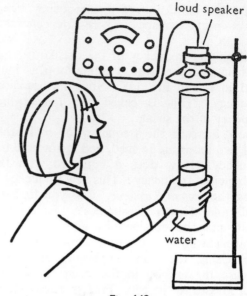

Fig. 162

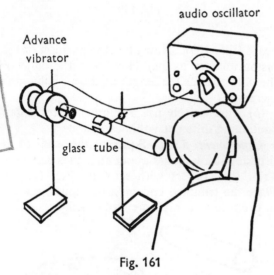

Fig. 161

(*b*) Having noted the fundamental frequency of the glass tube, continue increasing the oscillator frequency. Can you find any harmonics at which resonance also occurs? Write down those frequencies and state how they are related to the fundamental frequency.

Demonstration 5.17.

An alternative arrangement for studying resonance in closed pipes is shown in Fig. 162. Adjust the oscillator frequency until the loudest note is heard. When resonance occurs you should be able to detect a drop in loudness when the cylinder is *removed*.

Demonstration 5.18.

(*a*) Draw a piece of glass tubing into a long fine jet having an internal diameter between $\frac{1}{32}$ and $\frac{1}{16}$ of an inch and leave the end ragged. Use this tube to produce a gas flame about a

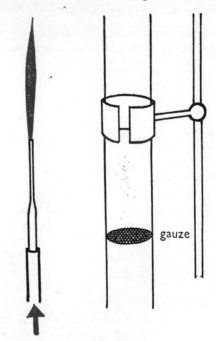

Fig. 163

foot long. Such a flame is sensitive to certain frequencies and will respond vigorously if a bunch of keys is shaken a few feet away. It will also respond to a high frequency note (5–10 kilocycles) from an audio oscillator. The bore of the tube and the size of the flame are rather critical, however, and you may have to try various tubes to obtain satisfactory results. In this experiment enough energy is being transmitted by the sound waves to cause the flame to fluctuate.

(b) Fix a small piece of ordinary wire gauze about 6 inches from the bottom of a long glass tube and heat the centre of the gauze with the gas jet. Remove the flame and listen. Repeat this experiment with a shorter tube and say why the note heard is different. When the tube is singing turn it until it is horizontal. What happens? Turn it until it is vertical again. What happens?

Fig. 164

Experiment 5.19. If you blow across the mouth of a milk bottle you can produce standing waves. A little practice is required to obtain the best results. Once you have succeeded in producing a good loud note, ask a friend to listen at the mouth of an identical milk bottle. Does the second bottle 'amplify' the note heard by your friend? Why?

Experiment 5.20. Examine as many wind instruments as possible, including some plastic whistles. What causes the air to vibrate in each of them? In a pipe organ which pipes produce the low notes?

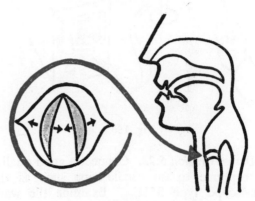

Fig. 165

Speech

Our vocal cords consist of two pairs of flaps, one above the other. When we breathe out they vibrate and produce sound waves. Muscles control the size and shape of our vocal cords and also alter their tension. It is these muscles which control the frequency of the sound produced. Our mouth and nose cavities act as resonators which amplify certain frequencies more than others.

Experiment 5.21.

(a) Place your forefinger and thumb on either side of your Adam's apple. Now make a low pitched sound. Can you detect any vibration? Throat microphones use these vibrations.

(b) Sing the *same* note to ah, eh, ay, oh, oo. These notes have different *qualities*.

Quality

If a violin, a trumpet and a pipe organ were playing the same note would you be able to identify the different instruments? To discover the way in which those sounds differ you should study the shape of the waves produced.

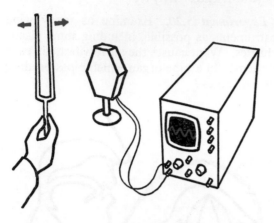

Fig. 166

Demonstration 5.22. Connect a good quality microphone to an oscilloscope such as the Serviscope type S51E$_{28}$. Examine the wave pattern produced by a tuning fork held close to the microphone. Compare this pattern with that produced by a good quality audio oscillator.

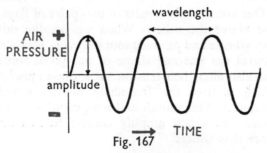

Fig. 167

A wave of this shape is called a *sine wave*. It is the simplest form of sound wave and is sometimes referred to as a *pure tone*.

Warning! The pattern on the oscilloscope screen (Fig. 167) is a *graph* drawn automatically by an electron beam. It is produced in a similar way to the picture on a T.V. screen. Do not confuse this graph, which is a transverse

wave pattern, with the sound waves which produce it. They are longitudinal waves.

Demonstration 5.23.

(*a*) Use an oscilloscope to examine the wave forms produced by various instruments such as a guitar, a piano, a cornet, a flute, an organ pipe or a whistle. Do the waves have the same shape as those obtained from the tuning fork?

(*b*) Some audio oscillators produce sine waves and square waves. If possible listen to the note produced by each and examine its wave form on an oscilloscope.

(*c*) Sing again 'ah, eh, ee, oh, oo' and see the shapes produced.

The last experiments have shown that, although the frequency of various notes may be the same, the waves can have different shapes. This difference in wave form is responsible for the characteristic sound (quality) of each instrument. Mathematicians have shown that any shape of wave can be split up into a sine wave of the same fundamental frequency and a number of harmonics (overtones) of different sizes (amplitudes).

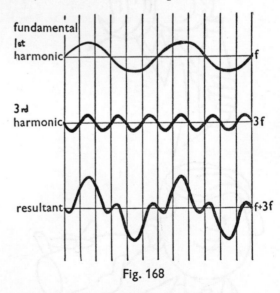

Fig. 168

By adding together the fundamental and one or more higher harmonics a completely different wave form is obtained. The first and third harmonics are added in Fig. 168. It is the number and the amplitude of the harmonics which give each instrument its distinctive *quality*. A violinist can alter slightly the quality of the note produced by bowing a string at different distances from the bridge. *How does a guitar player change the quality of the note produced?* (*11*)

Taking middle C as 256 cycles per second, the second harmonic is 512 cycles per second, the third 768 cycles per second and so on. If several audio oscillators are available you can alter the quality of a note at will.

Demonstration 5.24. Feed the outputs of several audio oscillators into a loudspeaker. Set one oscillator at, say, 256 c/s and the others at harmonic frequencies. By varying the outputs of the oscillators, the amplitudes of the harmonics present will alter, thus changing the quality of the note produced.

What carries sound energy?

1. Air

Most of the sounds we hear reach our ears through the air. As they pass through the air the sound waves carry energy with them. This was demonstrated by the fluctuations of a sensitive flame due to a high sound frequency.

The power transmitted by sound waves is normally very small compared with the power used by electric lights or heaters. The power required to heat a small room with, for example, a one-bar electric radiator is about 1,000 watts. To light the same room 100 watts is adequate, whereas 1 watt or less will fill the room with sound.

Experiment 5.25.

(*a*) Open the lid of a grand piano and produce a loud note either by singing or by playing an instrument such as a trumpet (Fig. 169). The string whose resonant frequency corresponds to the note produced should vibrate in sympathy. If you lay a very small piece of paper over the middle of the string and produce a loud enough note the paper will jump off. How did the energy necessary to lift the paper reach the piano string?

(*b*) Alternatively you can cause a guitar string to vibrate by playing a trumpet note close to it.

Fig. 169

(*c*) Gently press down and hold the middle C, G, C′ keys on a piano. Now play the C below middle C. Can you hear the notes C, G, C′?

Demonstration 5.26. Place a candle with a small flame immediately in front of an old 3 ohm loudspeaker. Connect the speaker for a few seconds to a 12 V A.C. supply. The sound energy should blow out the candle.

2. Water

Three hundred years ago Von Guericke found that fish were attracted by the sound of a bell rung under the water. Fishermen today use electronic 'beepers' to attract fish to their nets. Some fish, it is claimed, swim around in pairs when appropriate music is played to them!

Experiment 5.27.

(*a*) If you like swimming under water, try this experiment. Ask a friend to knock together two stones below the surface while you listen for the noise. One work of warning—you should not be too close to the stones as your eardrums could be damaged by the sound waves.

(*b*) Place a squeaking toy in a polythene bag and hold it in a bucket of water. Can you hear it squeak when you squeeze it? Put your ear to the side of the bucket and try again.

Demonstration 5.28.

(a) Connect a low resistance headphone to an audio oscillator. Place the headphone in a polythene bag and tie the neck of the bag tightly to prevent water getting in. Now slowly lower the headphone into a bucket of water. Can the note still be heard?

amplifier

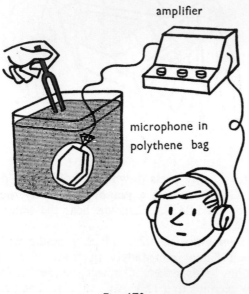

microphone in polythene bag

Fig. 170

(b) The headphone used in the last experiment can now be used as a microphone. Connect it to the input of an amplifier and find out if it will detect any sound when (1) the side of the container is tapped or (2) the water surface is touched with the prongs of a vibrating tuning fork. Do the results of these experiments show that sound travels through water?

3. Solids

Sound waves can travel through gases and liquids. Can they also travel through solids? First let us see if compression waves can be transmitted through solids.

Experiment 5.29.

(a) Firmly grip a metal bar in a vice and suspend a metal ball so that it touches one end as shown in Fig. 171. Tap the other end with a hammer and note the result.

(b) Lay three pennies in a row so that they touch each other. Hold the centre penny firmly and tap it with one of the others. What happens to the third penny?

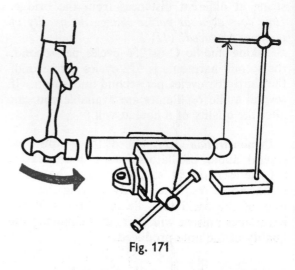

Fig. 171

In each of the above cases energy was transmitted through the metals, although they themselves did not move. Let us now see if sound waves can travel through metals and other solids.

Experiment 5.30.

(a) Place one end of a pencil or piece of dowelling in your ear and let the other end touch a ticking clock.

(b) Repeat the above experiment, using similar rods of metal, rubber and Plasticine.

(c) Tie a spoon to one end of a length of string and hold the other end in your ear. Allow the spoon to bump against a chair or table.

(d) Construct a toy telephone, using two tin cans and, say, fifteen feet of fine wire or string. Draw a sketch of the apparatus and explain how it works.

Do these experiments suggest that sound travels through solids?

Experiment 5.31.
You can test the ability of different solids to carry sound by using a tuning fork and a number of solids such as paper, glass, iron, wood, plastic, felt, rubber and cork. Each material should be about a quarter

Fig. 172

now see if sound waves will pass through a vacuum.

Demonstration 5.33. Attach a small battery to an electric bell and suspend them by elastic thread inside a bell jar. Switch on the bell and place the jar on the plate of a vacuum pump.

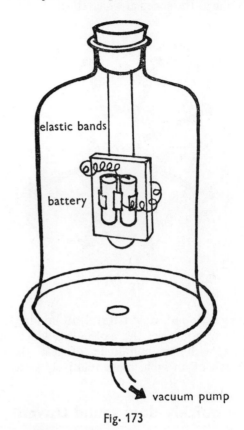

elastic bands

battery

vacuum pump

Fig. 173

of an inch thick. Touch the base of the vibrating tuning fork to a desk and listen carefully to the loudness of the sound produced. Now repeat this experiment placing the materials, one at a time, between the fork and the desk. How do they affect the sound produced?

Experiment 5.32. Hold one end of a pencil in your mouth without touching it with your teeth. Tap or scratch the other end of the pencil. What do you hear? Now hold the pencil firmly with your teeth and repeat the experiment. Is there any difference in the sound heard? In the second case sound was transmitted through your teeth and the bones in your head to your ears.

If you have had your voice recorded, even on a first class recorder, you probably exclaimed, 'That's not me!' the first time you heard it. Your friend, however, may have said it was 'just like you'. *Can you explain this difference of opinion? (12)*

4. Vacuum

We have discovered that sound waves travel through solids, liquids and gases. We must

Can you hear the bell ringing? Pump out the air from the jar. Can you still hear the bell? Even if all the air were removed and no sound were transmitted through the vacuum might you expect to hear the bell faintly? Why?

Sound waves, then, can be sent through matter but they cannot be transmitted through a vacuum. When a source vibrates, the molecules of matter around it are pushed and pulled so that the material is alternately compressed and rarefied. The compressions and the rarefactions travel outwards from the source rather like expanding shells (Fig. 174). In the air the shells can be thought of as spheres around the source. The molecules vibrate to and fro in the direction in which the wave is moving. *What are such waves called?* (*13*) As in the case of water waves, the speed at which the sound waves travel outwards is not the same as the speed at which the molecules are

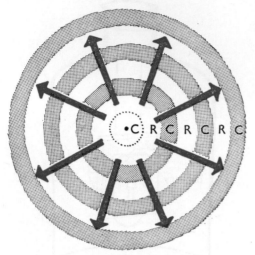

Fig. 174

moving. Sound waves travel at hundreds of miles per hour, yet the molecules, which may vibrate with an amplitude of less than a millionth of an inch, move relatively slowly.

How quickly does sound travel?

1. Sound in Air

Over three hundred years ago Martin Mersenne, a Franciscan friar, found that sound travels in air at about 1,000 feet per second. He used pulse beats to time echoes. It was not until about the beginning of the 18th century that accurate observations were made in England. The Vicar of Upminster timed the interval between the flash of a cannon fired 13 miles away and the arrival of the sound. He used a pendulum to measure the time intervals.

There are many ways of measuring the speed of sound in air. You should know *one* of them.

Experiment 5.34.

(*a*) Like Mersenne you can use echoes, provided you find a wide open, preferably grassy, space with only one building or wall near it which will reflect the sound. On a calm day take up a position about 100 yards from the

Fig. 175

building and clap two blocks of wood together. Can you hear a reflected sound (echo)? Continue clapping with a steady rhythm so that you hear clap-echo-clap-echo. Adjust your rate of clapping until the time interval between a clap and its echo is the same as the interval between an echo and the next clap. Having become expert at such clapping ask a friend to measure the time for, say, 50 claps. Whilst you clap he should count '3, 2, 1, 0, 1, 2, 3 . . .', starting the watch on the *zero*.

You will have to think out the calculation very carefully. Suppose the time for 50 claps was 100 seconds. What would be the time interval between claps? What would be the time taken for the sound to travel *to and from* the wall? Are you sure? If the wall were 180 yards from the clapper, what would be the speed of sound? Use this result to find the air speed of a plane travelling at Mach 2.

(*b*) The Vicar of Upminster was probably in a better position than most of us to have a annon fired! Nevertheless, you can adopt his method, using a starting pistol fired a mile or o from the observer. If you are in Edinburgh, ou can use the 1 o'clock gun fired at the castle, rovided you can find a position from which to ee the flash or the smoke and hear the report. The time interval between them should be measured with a stop watch. You must either measure the distance to the gun or calculate it rom a large scale map. What assumption are you making about the speed of light? Why is his assumption reasonable?

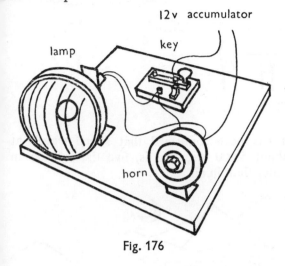

Fig. 176

(c) If you have easy access to a large sports field this method is simple and provides a good excuse to spend a period in the open air.

A car horn and headlamp are attached to a board and wired in parallel. They are supplied by a 12 volt car battery and switched by means of a morse key. The operator should practise switching the lamp and horn on and off, using a metronome so that they are 'on' for the same length of time as they are 'off'. A suitable switching speed is 'on' and 'off' for a quarter of a second each, thus giving two flashes per second.

The apparatus should be set up at one end of the field and switched on and off. Standing beside the apparatus, you will see the flash and hear the blast at the same time. If now you move away from the equipment you will eventually reach a point where the blasts are heard *between* the flashes. At two flashes per second how long is the sound taking to travel to you? Measure the distance from the sources.

Continue walking away from the lamp and horn until you again see the flash and hear the blast at the same time. At two flashes per second how long is the sound now taking to travel to you? Again find out how far you are away from the sources.

To find out the exact number of flashes per second you should use a stop watch to time the metronome over 50 swings. Count '3, 2, 1, 0, 1, 2, 3 . . . ' starting the watch on the 'zero'. Calculate the speed of sound in air from both results.

If you hear a roar of thunder 10 seconds after seeing a lightning flash, what can you conclude? (*14*) *What assumption have you made?* (*15*)

Speed and frequency

If you have listened to a band playing in the distance, or heard music or speech coming from a distant public address system, you will realise that, although the sound took several seconds to reach you, *all* the frequencies arrived at the right time. Had the high notes arrived before the low, or the loud notes before the soft, both music and speech would have been unrecognisable. We conclude then that the speed at which sound travels does not depend either on the frequency (pitch) or the amplitude (loudness).

Speed and temperature

The wavelength of the note produced by a whistle is determined by the physical length of the whistle. *If the velocity of the sound were suddenly to be* increased *and the wavelength remained the same, how would the pitch of the note produced be affected?* (*16*) The answer to this question should enable you to find out how the velocity of sound in air is affected when the air is heated.

Experiment 5.35. Blow a whistle using an electric blower and two pieces of rubber tubing as shown in Fig. 177. A whistle producing a single note is most suitable. In one of the tubes insert three feet of half inch copper tube and heat it with several bunsen burners. When a steady note is obtained, close the tubes alternately by squeezing them at A or B. Does the note vary? Is its frequency higher or lower with hot air? What does this tell you about the velocity of sound in hot air? Is hot air denser or less dense than cold air?

In more recent experiments an underwater charge is exploded. The sound produced is picked up by various waterproofed microphones attached to buoys whose positions are accurately known. By measuring the time taken for the sound waves to reach the microphones

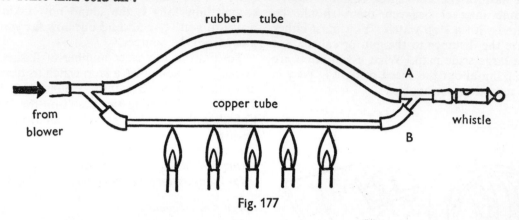

Fig. 177

Speed and material

We have considered the speed of sound in air. Does it travel at the same speed in other gases?

Experiment 5.36. Connect one end of a long length of bunsen tubing to a gas pipe and attach a whistle to the other end. Turn on the gas and listen to the note. What happens when the coal gas reaches the whistle? Remembering that the wavelength of the sound is determined by the length of the whistle (which doesn't alter) what does the change in note tell you about the speed of sound in coal gas? Is coal gas denser or less dense than air?

Remove the rubber tube from the gas pipe and blow through it. What happens?

2. Sound in Liquids

Just over a hundred years ago two Swiss scientists measured the speed of sound in water. One sat in a boat at one end of Lake Geneva. He struck a hammer against a bell, situated below the water, when a charge of gunpowder exploded. His friend was in another boat a mile away, listening through an ear trumpet for the clang of the bell. He measured the time interval between his seeing the flash of gunpowder and hearing the bell.

it has been confirmed that sound travels at about 5,000 ft/s, that is, five times faster in water than in air.

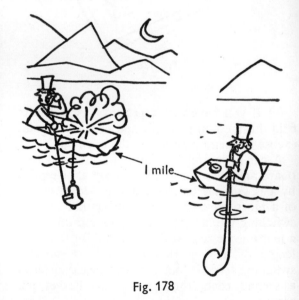

Fig. 178

3. Sounds in Solids

You have already found that sound travels through solids. The following experiment will enable you to discover whether it travels more quickly in iron or air.

Experiment 5.37. To compare the speed of sound in air and iron send a sound pulse through iron railings. Ask a friend to strike the railings with a stone while you listen to the sound at a point on the railings about 30 yards away. If you touch the railings with the point

Fig. 179

of a pencil and place the other end in your ear you will be able to hear the sound which has travelled through the railings. The sound of the blow will also be transmitted through the air. Which sound do you hear first? Accurate experiments have shown that sound travels about fifteen times faster in iron than in air.

What happens to transmitted sound?

(i) Reflection

One of the experiments used to find the speed of sound relied on the reflection of a pulse from a wall about 100 yards from the source. Such a reflection of sound is called an *echo*. If the reflection comes from a wall which is less than 50 feet from the source, a separate echo cannot be detected; instead, the original noise appears to have been prolonged. Sound reflections within buildings, particularly large halls, are extremely troublesome, and great care has to be taken by architects to avoid unwanted sound reflections. Walls are often covered with sound absorbing material to reduce such reflection. If you visit St. Paul's Cathedral in London, or the Mausoleum in Hamilton, you will be able to hear the results of some quite amazing sound reflections.

Demonstration 5.38.

(*a*) Fix a low resistance earphone into the end of a 15 inch cardboard tube and use an audio oscillator to feed a 3,500 c/s note into it. Use a similar tube and earphone to pick up the reflected note, and pass the signal into a valve voltmeter or a tape recorder. The recording level meter can be used to indicate the strength of the sound received. Alternatively an amplifier may be used and the output fed into headphones or an oscilloscope.

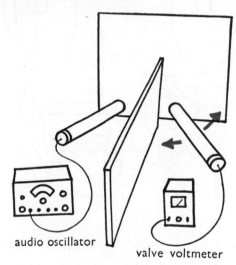

audio oscillator   valve voltmeter

Fig. 180

Place a board in front of the open ends of the tubes as shown in Fig. 180, and rotate the pickup tube until the maximum sound is detected. Compare the angles of incidence and reflection when the maximum signal is obtained.

(*b*) Replace the board with other substances such as metal, glass, cardboard, cloth, cork or fibre glass. Can you discover which substances reflect most and which reflect least sound?

Experiment 5.39.

(a) Place a watch which ticks fairly loudly at the focus of one parabolic reflector[16] and a microphone at the focus of another (Fig. 181). The output of the microphone should be amplified and fed to a pair of headphones. The watch can be heard over 10 to 20 feet provided there are no other noises in the room!

(b) Try to devise a similar experiment at home, using two umbrellas as reflectors. You should be able to hear the tick of a small alarm clock over a fair distance provided you place it and your ear at the correct places!

irregular motion of the particles in the absorber shows itself as an increase in temperature. When sound waves strike the walls of a room, for example, they are partially absorbed, causing the temperature of the walls to rise very slightly.

(ii) Refraction

When plane water waves were passed over a 'lens shaped' glass plate they were brought to a focus. The following demonstration should enable you to see if sound waves can be focused when they pass through a 'lens' which slows them down.

Fig. 181

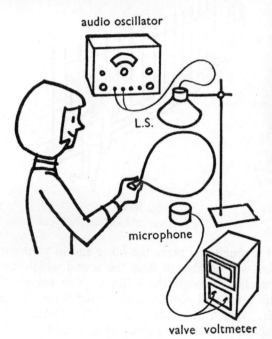

Fig. 182

Sound travels easily through tubes because of the reflections from the inner walls. A doctor's stethoscope depends on this type of sound transmission. Bats navigate by sending out waves which are reflected from solid objects. They then catch the echoes in their large and very sensitive ears.

While some materials reflect most of the sound striking them, others absorb a great deal of the sound energy. Felt, for example, absorbs about half of the sound energy which reaches it. When sound is absorbed the regular motion of the particles in the sound wave is changed into irregular motion. This

Demonstration 5.40. A loudspeaker or earphone is supplied with a 3,500 cycle note from an oscillator and placed about a foot above a microphone as shown in Fig. 182. The microphone is connected to a valve-voltmeter, tape recorder or oscilloscope acting as an indicator of volume level.

(a) Place a balloon filled with carbon dioxide between the speaker and the microphone, and note any change in the level of the sound picked up. A piece of 'dry ice' pushed into a balloon will soon fill it with carbon dioxide.

(b) Repeat the experiment, using a balloon filled with coal gas. Do the results suggest that sound waves are focused by the balloon filled with carbon dioxide? Were the waves focused by coal gas? How does the speed of sound in these gases compare with its speed in air?

WARM DAY

Warm surface heats the air and sound travels more quickly.

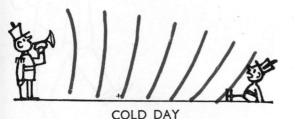

COLD DAY

Cold surface cools the air and sound moves more slowly.

Fig. 183

Sound waves are bent when the speed at which part of the wavefront is travelling is altered. This change in direction is called *refraction*. On a warm day the Earth's surface warms the air in contact with it so that the speed of sound near the ground is increased. Sound waves, therefore, tend to be bent away from the earth so that sound does not carry so well in hot weather.

On a cold day or night the layer of air near the earth is cold and the speed of sound is reduced. Sound waves are therefore bent down towards the earth, and sounds can be heard over long distances under such conditions.

(iii) Diffraction

Water waves were seen to be bent when they passed through a narrow slit. Will sound waves do the same?

Demonstration 5.41. Feed the output of an audio oscillator into a loudspeaker, using an amplifier if necessary. Place two boards, about a metre square, in front of the speaker as shown in Fig. 184. Connect a microphone to a sound level indicator.

audio oscillator

valve
voltmeter

Fig. 184

Set the oscillator to 100 c/s and slowly move the microphone across and beyond the opening. Carefully observe any change in sound level at or beyond the edges of the opening.

Repeat this experiment using a 10 Kc/s note. What differences do you observe? Does sound bend round corners? What frequencies bend most?

Experiment 5.42. Stand in the middle of a large room and place one finger of your left hand in your right ear. Rub together your thumb and forefinger of your right hand so as to produce a *high pitched* sound a few inches to the right of your right ear. Can you hear the sound with your left ear? Why is this? Now move so that your left ear is as near to a corner of the room as possible. Repeat the experiment and explain the results you obtain.

Try the experiment again, using a bunch of keys to produce a lower frequency noise when you shake them. Can you explain any differences observed?

These experiments have shown us that low pitched notes bend easily, although high pitched notes do not bend nearly so much.

Fig. 185

The difference between the bending of high and low frequency sounds is evident near the top of a cliff. The low frequency noise of sea waves can be heard some distance from the edge of the cliff, but high frequency bird calls coming from the face of the cliff can be heard only near the edge.

What instruments in a military band can you still hear once the band has disappeared round a corner? (17) Which notes can you no longer hear? (18)

Most of the frequencies we normally listen to in speech and music do bend fairly readily so that we can hear sounds coming round a corner.

(iv) Interference

We have already seen that sound waves passing through two different lengths of rubber tubing will interfere with one another. It was, in fact, because of this that we concluded that sound was a type of wave motion. Here is another interference experiment.

Experiment 5.43. Place two similar loud-speakers about a metre apart and connect them to an audio-frequency oscillator. Adjust the oscillator to produce a note of about 5 Kc/s.

Walk slowly across the room, about two metres in front of the loudspeakers, listening with only the ear nearer the speakers as shown in Fig. 186. What do you hear and why?

Repeat the experiment using only one loud-speaker.

Fig. 186

Beats

If two sources send out notes at slightly different frequencies, they interfere with each other to produce variations in amplitude at a frequency equal to the difference between the two source frequencies.

Demonstration 5.44.

(*a*) Use two oscillators to feed two loud-speakers. Set one oscillator at, say, 250 c/s and slowly adjust the frequency of the other from 240 to 260 c/s. Can you detect the *beat frequency*? If only one oscillator is available record a note on tape and play it back together with the 'live' oscillator set to a slightly different frequency.

(*b*) Secure two tuning forks of the same frequency. Load the prongs of one fork with adhesive tape so that it vibrates slightly more slowly. Alternatively use 'standard' and 'normal' forks which are slightly different in pitch.

Can you detect a beat note when the forks are both vibrating?

(c) Beats may also be obtained from the notes produced by two long glass tubes of slightly different lengths (Demonstration 5.18 (b)).

How are sounds detected?

Sound energy is transmitted through the air by changes in pressure. The air molecules vibrate to and fro so that the air is compressed (greater pressure) and then rarified (smaller pressure). You have seen that vibrating air can blow out a candle, cause a piano string to vibrate or generate enough electricity to send messages over telephone wires. To produce this electric current the changes in air pressure caused a thin metal plate (diaphragm) to vibrate at the same frequency as the air itself.

Fig. 187

Experiment 5.45. Remove the top and bottom from a tin can or similar container. Stretch a piece of balloon rubber, not too tightly, over one end and attach a small piece of mirror, aluminium foil or polished metal near one edge of it. Project a narrow beam of light on to the mirror and catch the reflected light on a screen or wall. Speak loudly into the open end of the can and watch the reflected beam. What effect have the sound waves had on the rubber diaphragm?

The Ear

Most sound detectors are operated by sound waves causing a diaphragm to vibrate. In the ear (Fig. 188) sound waves are collected by the *outer ear* and then passed to the ear drum, a kind of diaphragm. The ear drum vibrates at the sound frequencies, and the movement is sent through a series of levers (anvil, hammer and stirrup) in the *middle ear* (shown in red).

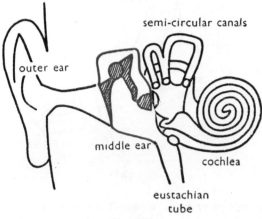

Fig. 188

The vibrations finally reach the *inner ear*, which is a shell-like coiled tube called the cochlea. This shell is filled with a fluid and contains thousands of tiny fibres of different lengths. These fibres, which respond to different frequencies, are linked to the brain through the auditory nerves. The eustachian tube, which comes into the middle ear, is connected to the throat and helps to balance the pressure on each side of the eardrum. The three semicircular canals, which are connected to the inner ear, play no part in hearing. They enable us to keep our balance.

Our hearing does not, however, depend only on the signals which are transmitted from the cochlea to the brain. As in the case of optical illusions, we interpret those signals in terms of our past experience and our desires. In what other way can you explain the fact that you do not 'hear' an alarm clock twelve inches from your ear, whereas, in school, a telephone or bicycle bell half a mile away prompts the immediate response 'Bell, Sir!'?

The Microphone

A microphone is a machine which transforms one kind of energy (sound) into another (electrical energy). This is done in a variety of ways in different microphones. For the moment we will consider only the ribbon microphone.

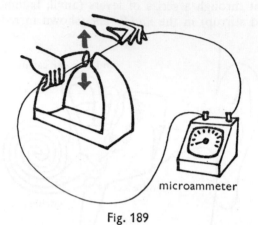

microammeter

Fig. 189

Experiment 5.46. Connect a wire to a micro-ammeter and move the wire up and down between the poles of a powerful magnet. What happens?

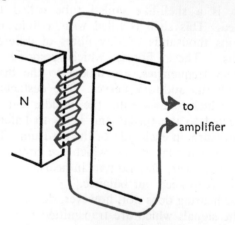

N

S

to
amplifier

RIBBON MICROPHONE

Fig. 190

In a ribbon microphone (Fig. 190) a thin corrugated ribbon of aluminium alloy is suspended between the poles of a powerful magnet. The ribbon vibrates to and fro in sympathy with the air, and thus generates minute electric currents which depend on the frequency and amplitude of the sound waves.

If a guitar string is plucked and the sound is picked up by a ribbon microphone, amplified and fed into a loudspeaker, what changes of energy are involved? (19) Can you discover what type of microphone is used in the mouthpiece of a telephone and in most popular tape recorders? (20) Why do you think it is essential to treat microphones with great care? (21)

Stored sound

(a) Disc

You cannot store sound! Just as you must change electrical energy to some other form, such as chemical energy, so you must change sound to some other form also if you want to store it.

Fig. 191

Experiment 5.47. Take an old 78 r.p.m. disc (they were called gramophone records in those days) and place it on a turntable. Hold a small sharp sewing needle on the revolving disc and listen. Now push the needle through a piece of card and hold it as shown in Fig. 191. What do you hear now? Examine the grooves with a powerful lens and see how the disc enables sound to be reproduced.

Modern record players often use crystal pickup heads. They depend on the fact that electrical voltages are produced by changes in pressure applied to quartz crystals. The needle transmits varying pressures to the crystal as the disc rotates.

(b) Film

If you examine a piece of sound film, you will see a strip down the edge called the *sound track*. A very narrow beam of light shines through this part of the film and then on to a photo-electric cell, which changes variations in light intensity into variations in electric current. These variations are amplified and fed into a loudspeaker situated near or behind the screen.

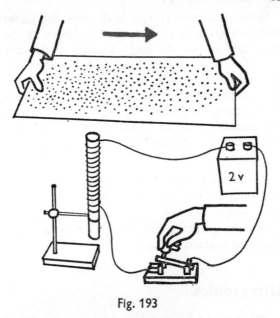

Fig. 193

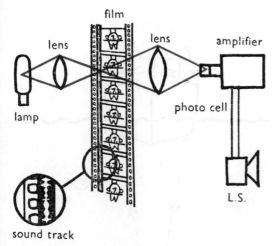

Fig. 192

Recording tape is coated with a layer of magnetic material. This tape passes over an electro-magnet which causes the direction of the atomic magnets on the tape to switch round, rather like the iron filings, as the current in the electro-magnet alters. The current in the electro-magnet is related to the frequency and amplitude of the sound entering the micro-phone. It thus produces a magnetic pattern of the sound.

(c) Tape

The development of tape recording within your lifetime has been so rapid that today practically all recordings are made originally on tape. The quality is so good that it is impossible to tell the difference between a live radio broadcast and a recorded programme. What is even more remarkable is that this is true of taped T.V. programmes as well as sound.

Experiment 5.48. Sprinkle some iron filings on a sheet of paper and move the paper over an electro-magnet, which you make by winding twenty turns of insulated wire round a bar of iron and connecting the ends to a 2 volt accumulator. While switching the magnet on and off, slowly move the sheet of paper over it. What happens to the iron filings?

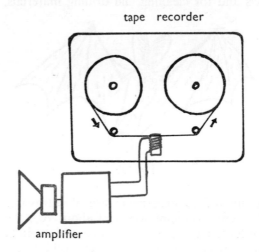

Fig. 194

When the tape is run back over the same electro-magnet it causes small voltages to be produced across the coil. These voltages are then fed into an amplifier and loudspeaker. The speed at which the tape runs over the electro-magnet (record/playback head) determines the quality of the sound recorded. Hi Fi enthusiasts use 15 or $7\frac{1}{2}$ inches per second, but lesser mortals are content with $3\frac{3}{4}$, $1\frac{7}{8}$ or even $\frac{15}{16}$ in/s.

Demonstration 5.49. Record a strong signal on a piece of magnetic tape. Now apply to the tape *Indicord*$_{17}$, an aqueous suspension of magnetic particles, in order to make the magnetic pattern visible.

Ultrasonics

What is the highest frequency you can hear? *(22)* If the frequency of a sound is increased beyond this limit are waves still transmitted? This question can be answered by watching a sensitive flame subjected to a very high frequency, or a dog responding to a Galton whistle producing a note of, say, 25 Kc/s, which you cannot hear. When the frequency of sound waves becomes too high for us to hear, the waves are referred to as *ultrasonic* waves. They behave as sound waves and have become extremely important in industry for detecting flaws and for cleaning and drilling materials.

Fig. 195

Long before man made use of ultrasonics, bats were producing waves of about 70,000 c/s in order to navigate. They send out high pitched sounds which are reflected from solid objects. From the time taken for the reflected sound to

return, the bats can tell just how far away the object lies.

Ships use a similar device to find the depth of the sea below them or to detect submarines or shoals of fish (Fig. 196). This echo sounding system, called *sonar*, produces ultrasonic waves electrically, using a vibrating crystal. *If the wavelength of such waves was 0·1 foot what would be their approximate frequency? (23)*

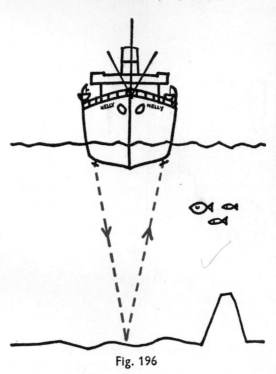

Fig. 196

Ultrasonics in Industry

The range of ultrasonic waves extends from about 20,000 c/s to thousands of millions of cycles per second. The higher frequency ultrasonic waves will not pass from a solid into air, so that any flaw in a material which contains a pocket of air will prevent the waves from passing. Ultrasonics may thus be used to detect flaws in, for example, a car tyre as shown in Fig. 197. In this case the third meter indicates the position of the flaw. When detecting cracks in metals the transmitting crystal (transducer) and the detector are on the same side of the metal casting. Waves are reflected at the flaws and picked up by the detector.

Ultrasonic drills can be made to cut holes of any shape or size as they do not rotate. The material to be drilled is first coated with carborundum paste which enables the vibrating drill to cut its way through. Dentists' drills are sometimes operated by ultrasonic waves.

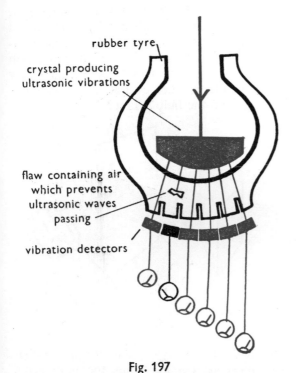

rubber tyre

crystal producing ultrasonic vibrations

flaw containing air which prevents ultrasonic waves passing

vibration detectors

Fig. 197

Ultrasonic waves are widely used for cleaning small pieces of intricate equipment such as watch movements or time switches. The apparatus need not be dismantled; it is simply immersed in a bath of liquid into which are passed the ultrasonic waves. The successive compressions and rarefactions produce tiny bubbles on the surface of the equipment being cleaned. As the bubbles burst, bits of dirt sticking to the surface or even lodged in cracks are shot away. Some dishwashing machines also operate on this principle.

Metals may be welded together using ultrasonic waves. The metals are held firmly together and one of them is then made to vibrate by bringing it into contact with an ultrasonic generator. This causes one metal to rub against the other producing enough heat to melt the metals at the point of contact. Aluminium and its alloys can now be soft soldered without flux, using ultrasonic waves to break up the oxide film which quickly forms on aluminium surfaces.

The number of uses for ultrasonic waves is continually growing. They are used to produce thorough and even mixing of such things as paints, chocolate, mayonnaise and face creams (not together!). The depth of fat on a pig can be measured using ultrasonic echo sounding, and rats and mice can be cleared from infested houses using high intensity ultrasonic waves.

Visual aids

Electro-magnetic radiation

CHAPTER 6

Model of a model

Earlier in the course we studied the peculiar properties of Potty Putty. Imagine now that you were to give a piece to someone who had never before heard of it and ask him to tell you what it is. He would probably squeeze it and stretch it and conclude that it was a kind of chewing gum. Later you might take a ball of Potty Putty and show it to someone else. This time, however, you decide not to allow him to touch it. You merely drop it so that he sees it bouncing. The second observer will probably tell you that it is a rubber ball. A third observer watching it being struck with a hammer might describe it as clay, whilst a fourth observer watching it 'flowing' might conclude that it is a kind of treacle.

Whenever we are confronted with a new phenomenon we try to describe it in terms of something with which we are familiar. Potty Putty does behave *in some ways* like chewing gum, but it also behaves *in some ways* like rubber, clay and treacle. We might refer to the chewing gum *model*, the rubber *model*, the clay *model*, and the treacle *model* of Potty Putty. For some purposes the 'chewing gum model' might be adequate: for other purposes a different model would be more appropriate.

In this chapter we will be dealing with electro-magnetic radiation. You have already studied waves in water and it is because *in some ways* electro-magnetic radiation behaves like water waves that we use a 'wave model' to describe it. Just as any one model is not enough fully to describe Potty Putty, so one model is not necessarily adequate to describe all the properties of electro-magnetic radiation. As in the case of water waves and sound waves, we will look for interference produced by electro-magnetic radiation to justify our use of the term 'waves'.

Experiment 6.1. Send a beam of white light, from a ray box, through a prism and project the spectrum on to a white card. Use an infra-red detector₄ to discover if there is any radiation *beyond* the visible part of the spectrum. How can you test whether or not the radiation is coming from the bulb? Is it?

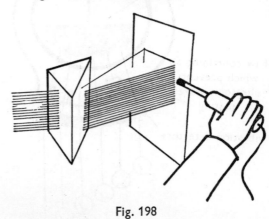

Fig. 198

From the above experiment it appears that there must be coming from the bulb some radiation which is in many ways similar to light yet is not visible. Scientists have discovered that visible light is only part of a great range of radiation which we call the electro-magnetic spectrum.

The electro-magnetic spectrum

The electro-magnetic spectrum extends from waves over ten kilometres (10^4 m) long to those having a wavelength of about a millionth of a millionth of a centimetre (10^{-14} m). The approximate wavelengths of various electro-magnetic waves are indicated in Fig. 199.

Electro-magnetic waves differ in the ways they are produced, used and detected. We will consider briefly each of the seven groups illustrated in Fig. 199.

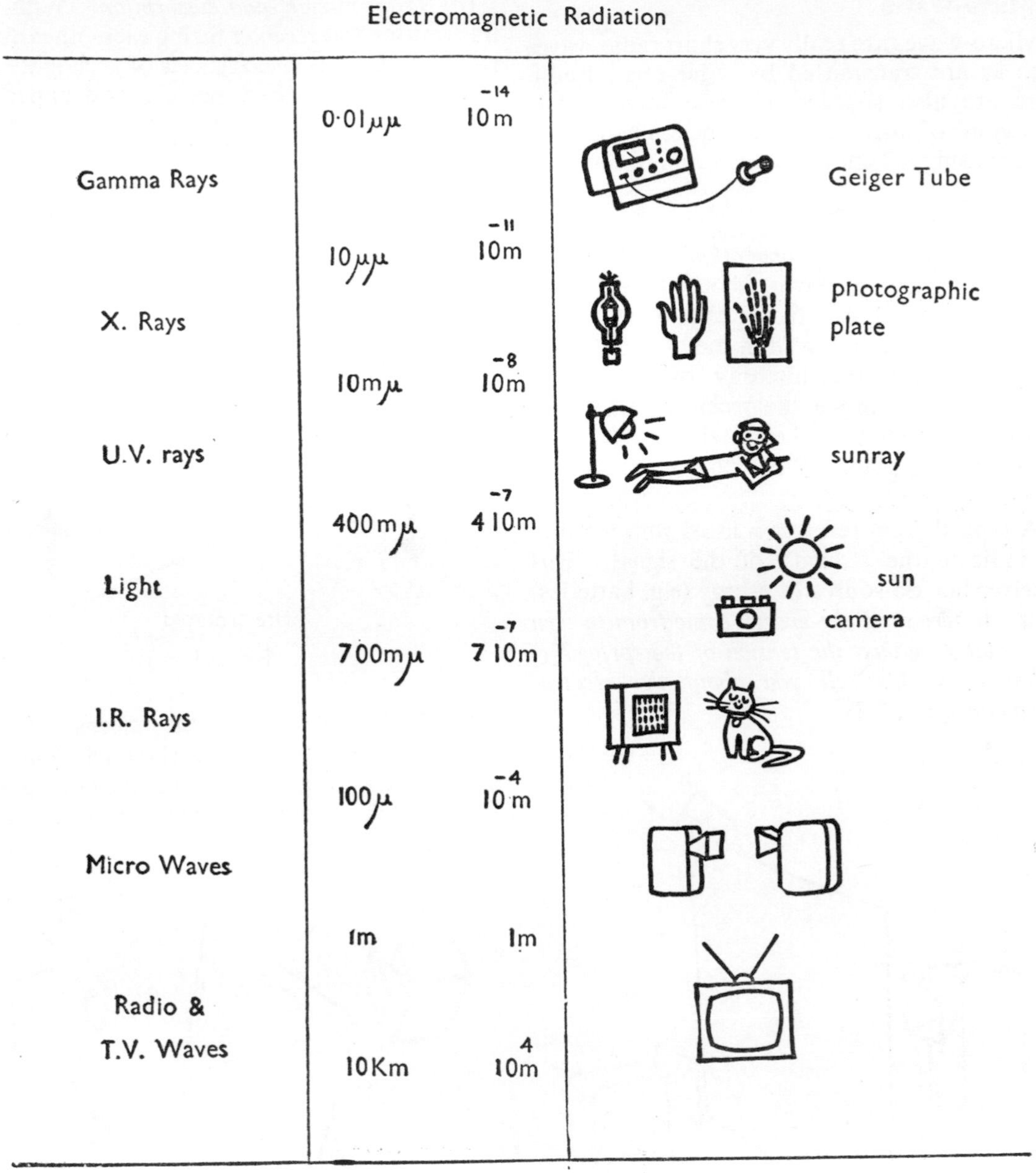

Electromagnetic Radiation

Gamma Rays	$0.01\mu\mu$ 10^{-14}m	Geiger Tube
X. Rays	$10\mu\mu$ 10^{-11}m	photographic plate
U.V. rays	$10m\mu$ 10^{-8}m	sunray
Light	$400m\mu$ 4×10^{-7}m	sun
	$700m\mu$ 7×10^{-7}m	camera
I.R. Rays		
Micro Waves	100μ 10^{-4}m	
Radio & T.V. Waves	$1m$ $1m$	
	$10Km$ 10^{4}m	

Fig. 199

1. Radio Waves

Experiment 6.2. Connect a battery to an electro-magnet such as an induction coil or an electric bell. Place a transistor radio a few feet away and listen to the effect produced when the electro-magnet is switched on and off.

Radio waves range in length from over 10 kilometres to less than 1 metre, including 'Your station of the stars' on 208 metres. Assuming the velocity of electro-magnetic radiation to be 3.10^8 m/s, find the wavelengths of the B.B.C. V.H.F. transmitters from the frequencies stated in the Radio Times.

4

2. Micro-Waves

Micro-waves are really very short radio waves such as are transmitted by radar sets. Radio stars are also sources of these waves. The behaviour of micro-waves can be easily demonstrated using a 3 cm transmitter and receiver[4,14].

Demonstration 6.3.

(a) *Straight line propagation.* Place the transmitter and receiver about two metres apart with their horns facing each other. They should be as far away from metal surfaces as possible. Note the intensity of the signal received. Now move the receiver to various positions and see how the signal strength varies from place to place. What do you conclude?

A typical 3 cm receiver is fitted with a meter to indicate the strength of the signal. This receiver has no source of energy (e.g. batteries) in it. *Where does the energy come from to turn the pointer against the tension of the spring?(1) What does this tell you about the electromagnetic waves?(2)*

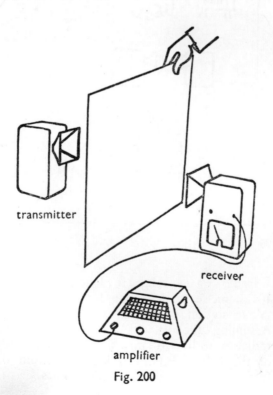

transmitter

receiver

amplifier

Fig. 200

(b) *Transmission and absorption.* With the transmitter and receiver facing each other about two metres apart, place sheets of such materials as metal, wood, glass, perspex and paper between them in turn. Which materials transmit most of the radiation? If no signal passes through the sheet, two explanations are possible. What are they?

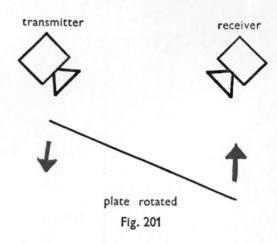

transmitter

receiver

plate rotated

Fig. 201

(c) *Reflection.* Place the horns of the transmitter and receiver as shown in Fig. 201 and rotate a metal plate in the position shown. When is the received signal greatest? What does this tell you?

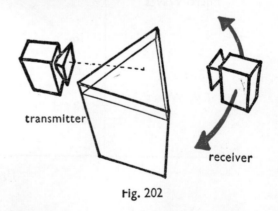

transmitter

receiver

Fig. 202

(d) *Refraction.* Fill a large perspex triangular container with paraffin and pass 3 cm waves into it as shown in Fig. 202. Move the receiver to and fro at the other side of the prism until the maximum signal is received. Now remove the prism and note any change in signal strength. Are the waves refracted by the prism? What does this tell you about the speed of 3 cm waves in paraffin?

(e) *Diffraction.* Construct a single slit by placing vertically two metal plates about 20 cm square with their surfaces facing and at right angles to the transmitter (Fig. 203). The slit should be about 1½ cm wide and 20 cm from the transmitter. Use a diode probe receiver to detect the waves as they pass through the slit. Is there any evidence to show that they bend round the edges of the slit?

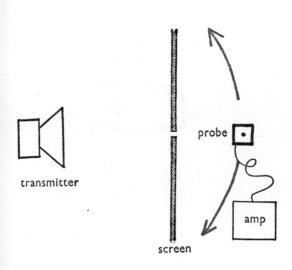

Fig. 203

How did the wavelength affect the bending of water waves around an obstacle? (3) Answer the following questions assuming that the same is true of electro-magnetic waves. *If you were designing a T.V. transmitter to be used in hilly country where the towns were built in the valleys, would you use the longest or the shortest wavelength which was practicable?* (4) *Why?* (5)

(f) *Interference.*

(i) Construct a 'double slit' from two large metal plates and one small one as shown in Fig. 204. Place the 3 cm transmitter about 50 cm from the double slit and detect the radiation on the other side with a diode probe.

How does the strength of the signal vary as the probe is moved from side to side? Why is this?

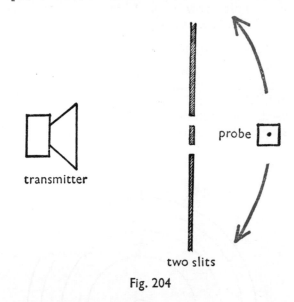

Fig. 204

(ii) Alternatively set up a diode probe about 30 cm from the transmitter and note the signal strength. Now move a metal reflector nearer to or further from the probe as shown in Fig. 205. Does the strength of the signal received ever become weaker than it was *without* the reflector in position? What does this suggest?

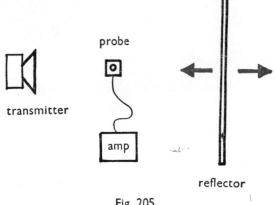

Fig. 205

Between micro-waves and infra-red radiation there is a small gap in the spectrum. This is the region of *sub-millimetre* waves. Until recently it was difficult, if not impossible, to produce these waves. Scientists are, however, now finding new ways of producing and using sub-millimetre waves.

3. Infra-Red Radiation

By the time the bars of a gas or electric fire are glowing red, infra-red rays are being given out. To detect the rays various devices may be used. They include photographic plates, thermoscopes, thermopiles and photo-transistors. The

changes from dull red to brilliant white. This happens when a current passes through the filament of an electric lamp.

Name three ways in which light can be detected? (6)

Light is produced by 'electron jumps' in the atoms of the source, for example, a bulb filament. Here is a simplified version of the model of the atom suggested by Niels Bohr.

Electrons are considered to move around the nucleus in certain regions or shells. The

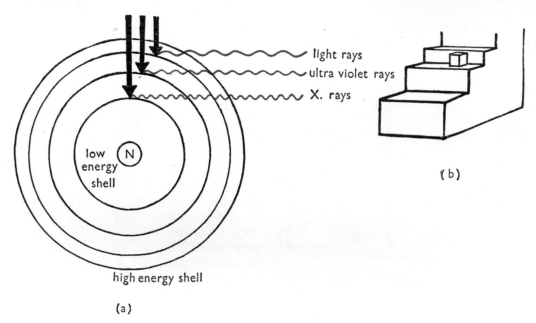

light rays
ultra violet rays
X. rays

low energy shell

N

high energy shell

(a)

(b)

Fig. 206

use of these detectors will be discussed in the next chapter.

4. Light Waves

Experiment 6.4. Connect a 12 volt car bulb to a 12 volt supply through a variable resistance. Watch the filament as the resistance is gradually reduced to zero.

At temperatures greater than 500°C solids start to emit visible radiation. As the temperature is raised still further the colour of the light

electrons in a shell near the nucleus have less energy than those in shells further away (Fig. 206(a)). Energy is therefore needed to move an electron from an inner shell to one further out.

Here is a gravitational analogy to help you understand these energy levels in an atom. Imagine a box sitting somewhere on a flight of steps (Fig. 206(b)). It possesses a certain amount of energy because of its position. *What is this energy called?* (7) If you raise the box to a higher step you have to do work. *Why?* (8) The box now possesses more energy.

If the box now fell down to a lower step it would lose energy. *Can you suggest some forms into which the energy might be changed?* (9)

If an electron is raised from a shell near the nucleus to an outer shell it then possesses more energy. This stored energy can be used to produce other forms of energy if the electron falls back to its original shell. To raise the electron to an outer shell requires energy, and this may be provided by heating the substance, or by bombarding the atom with fast moving electrons. When some of their electrons have been raised to their outer shells, atoms are said to have been *excited*. They do not remain in this state for long, however, and soon the electrons jump back into shells at lower energy levels. As they jump back energy is given out in the form of light waves, ultra-violet rays or X-rays (Fig. 206(*a*)). When an outer electron jumps to the next shell light is given out. With bigger electron jumps ultra-violet rays are emitted, and if an outer electron jumps back into the inner shell X-rays are produced.

5. Ultra-Violet Rays

Demonstration 6.5. Mercury vapour discharge tubes and arc lamps produce ultra-violet rays. Use some such source shining through a filter which allows only ultra-violet radiation to pass, to study various substances. You should include finger nails, teeth, vaseline, phosphors, anti-freeze, fluorescent paints and clothes washed in detergent. Can you explain in terms of the atomic model how *invisible* ultra-violet radiation makes the atoms in fluorescent paint radiate *visible* light?

Strong ultra-violet rays are radiated from the sun but a layer of ozone in the Earth's atmosphere absorbs most of them. Those which penetrate the atmosphere are responsible for producing sunburn. As glass also absorbs a fair amount of ultra-violet radiation, you are not likely to become sunburnt in a greenhouse. The longer wavelength ultra-violet rays stimulate the production of vitamins in the skin and have beneficial effects. Rays of shorter wavelength are, however, dangerous and because of this you should avoid staring at ultra-violet

sources. They are used in hospitals and food warehouses to kill harmful bacteria.

Photographic films can be used to detect ultra-violet radiation.

6. X-Rays

Demonstration 6.6. Study the pattern produced on a fluorescent screen by X-rays passing through various objects before reaching the screen. Remember that X-rays are dangerous and you should not be exposed to them for more than a few seconds.

X-rays are produced when fast moving electrons strike a solid and are rapidly decelerated. There are high energy (hard) X-rays and low energy (soft) X-rays. The hard X-rays are produced by X-ray tubes which have been very thoroughly evacuated; the small amount of gas remaining in them is at a very low pressure. Such tubes require high voltages to operate them and they produce rays harmful to the body. Such rays are used in the treatment of cancer. Tubes in which the gas is at a higher pressure require smaller voltages to produce soft X-rays. These are used to take X-ray photographs.

Today X-rays are used extensively in medicine and in industry. They detect flaws in castings and forgings. They show up alterations in old paintings, as do infra-red and ultra-violet rays. If passed through crystals, X-rays are deflected by the atoms enabling scientists to work out how the atoms are arranged (See Book 1, page 48). X-ray microscopes have now been developed which can be used beyond the limit of any optical microscope. They also allow us to study the inside of opaque materials.

7. Gamma Rays

Demonstration 6.7. A Geiger tube connected to a counter will detect gamma radiation. Hold the luminous dial of a watch close to such a tube and note the result. Within the luminous paint there is a radio-active material which gradually changes into another material and in so doing emits gamma rays.

Particle accelerators, such as cyclotrons, are used to fire high energy particles at atomic nuclei. The bombarded nucleus disintegrates, emitting sub-atomic particles and gamma rays. Gamma rays are also produced by some naturally radioactive materials, such as radium, when they decay. It is the gamma radiation from radium that is used in the treatment of cancer.

Visual aids

Charts

　Electromagnetic Spectrum[38,39]

The visible spectrum

CHAPTER 7

Models again

About three hundred years ago the Dutch scientist Christian Huyghens suggested that light was a wave motion. Sir Isaac Newton disagreed with him, and suggested that light consists of particles which are shot out from the source rather like bullets.

Light reaches us from the sun and therefore travels through empty space. Although it is relatively easy to understand waves on water or even in air, it is not so easy to picture waves in nothing! We have seen, however, that light can produce an interference pattern. This suggests that *in some ways* light does behave like water waves. Particles moving in the same direction could hardly cancel each other. Work with low intensities of light has, on the other hand, shown that light can also behave as if it were made of particles. These particles are now called *photons* and are sometimes described as 'bundles of energy'.

The wave model and the particle model are no longer regarded as rivals but rather as friends. They combine in the *quantum theory*, and together contribute to our understanding of the nature of light.

The wavelengths visible part of the electro-magnetic spectrum range from 400 to 700 millimicrons approximately (1 mμ = 10^{-9} m). Although this is a very small part of the total range of electromagnetic waves, it is for us the most important part of all, for these are the waves by which we see. We will now consider how light waves are produced, propagated and then detected.

How is light produced?

Light waves are radiated from atoms which have been excited. *What does this mean? (1)*

What must happen to such an atom before it emits light? (2) Energy of some kind is required in order to excite the atoms, and this can come from a variety of sources.

Flames

Light from candles, paraffin lamps and other flames is produced from chemical energy. During burning, heat is produced and tiny specks of carbon are thrown into the air. These carbon particles are heated so strongly that they glow yellow, that is, emit light. Can you explain why the carbon particles *rise* as black smoke?

Filaments

Electrical energy is used to heat tungsten filaments in electric lamps. As the temperature increases, the colour of the filament changes until the filament is white hot.

Stars

The energy in the light coming from the sun and the stars is derived from nuclear reactions. Enormous quantities of electro-magnetic radiation, ranging from gamma rays to radio waves, are emitted from such sources. Fortunately we are protected from the sun's more harmful radiation by our atmosphere. *What types of electro-magnetic rays from the sun can be detected on the Earth's surface? (3)*

Discharge Tubes

The sources we have considered so far produce heat as well as light. Gas discharge tubes and fluorescent lamps produce light and practically no heat. Such sources are therefore much more efficient than tungsten lamps. *Explain exactly what is meant here by 'efficient'. (4)*

95

Demonstration 7.1.

(a) Apply a high voltage from an induction coil across a discharge tube filled with air. Gradually evacuate the tube in darkness and watch the results produced. Why is there a visible glow?

(b) Tubes are often evacuated and then filled with an inert gas such as neon, helium, xenon or argon. Study at least one such tube in operation.

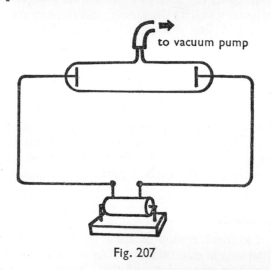

Fig. 207

Street lights often use tubes containing sodium vapour or mercury vapour. Fluorescent tubes also contain mercury vapour. When high-speed electrons strike the mercury atoms ultra-violet radiation is emitted. This radiation then strikes the fluorescent powder on the inside of the tube, causing the emission of visible light.

Light is a form of energy. Our eyes detect this energy, which comes either from a luminous or an illuminated source. Lamp filaments, candles, neon and fluorescent tubes are all examples of luminous sources. Most of the light which enters our eyes is, however, reflected. A body from which light is reflected is said to be illuminated. The moon is an example of an illuminated source. *Can you name others?* (5) You can see this page, your hands, the floor, the walls—in fact everything that is not itself a luminous source—because light is reflected from all of these *into* your eyes.

State whether the following are luminous or illuminated sources of light. (a) *A planet.* (b) *A T.V. screen.* (c) *A star.* (6)

Light when it reaches a substance, may pass through it, be reflected, or be absorbed by it. *Can a single substance transmit, reflect and absorb light?* (7) *Give some examples.* (8)

You can see through *transparent* substances such as glass. Light passes through frosted glass, yet you cannot see through it. Such a substance is said to be *translucent*. If no light passes through a substance it is said to be *opaque*.

How does light travel?

Straight Line Propagation

Demonstration 7.2.

(a) Paint the inside of an old balance case or similar box with matt black paint, leaving a small window at either end and the glass front clear. Fill the box with smoke and use a slide projector to pass a beam of light into one of the windows as shown in Fig. 208. Can you see the beam? Are the edges of the beam straight? What test would you use to see if they were straight?

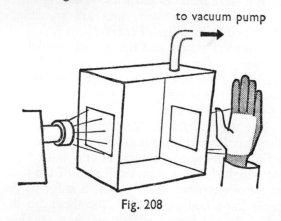

Fig. 208

(b) Remove the smoke from the box, using a vacuum pump and see what happens to the light beam. Is the beam passing through the box now? How would you test your answer? Can you explain the changes?

Experiment 7.3. Place a sheet of paper so that the sun's rays shine at right angles on to it.

If now you allow your hand to cast a shadow on the paper, what can you say about the shape and size of the shadow? What does this tell you about the rays of light from the sun?

Experiment 7.4. Use a shoe box or tin can to build a pinhole camera. Replace one end of the box with a sheet of tissue paper and pierce a pinhole in the other. Describe the results you obtain.

If we have a very small source of light, or if the source is very far away, it may be referred to as a *point source. Why is this not a strictly accurate description? (9)* A point source will cast sharp shadows. *What does this suggest? (10) Find the meaning of the words umbra and penumbra. (11)*

We usually represent *rays* of light by straight lines and refer to a collection of rays as a *beam* of light. *Can you draw a converging and a diverging beam of light? (12)*

For most practical purposes, although not all, it is sufficiently accurate to assume that light travels in straight lines.

Draw a sketch showing how an eclipse of the sun is produced, and indicate where a partial eclipse would be visible. (13) You will have to draw the sun as a large source. *How would your sketch differ if the sun were really a point source? (14)*

Reflection

Experiment 7.5. Set up on a sheet of paper a cylindrical lens in front of a ray box$_{2,15,16}$ as shown in Fig. 209. Adjust the position of the lens to produce a narrow parallel beam of light. Place a mirror on the paper so that the light strikes it as shown. Now mark on the paper the incident ray, the reflected ray, the normal and the position of the mirror surface. Measure the angles of incidence and reflection. How do they compare? Repeat the experiment with different angles of incidence.

Model 7.6. Drop a handful of table tennis balls on a perfectly flat surface and then on a very rough surface. Is there any difference in the way they bounce?

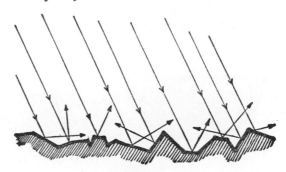

Fig. 210

Apart from the regular type of reflection which occurs at mirror surfaces, light is reflected from all kinds of surfaces. Most surfaces if viewed through a microscope would appear rather like Fig. 210, so that light is reflected in all directions. It is because light is reflected from objects that we see them. If no light is reflected from an object, the object cannot be seen. *What kind of surface reflects most light? (15)*

Refraction

Demonstration 7.7.

(a) Half fill a round-bottomed flask with water, and add a few drops of liquid Lux and a little fine aluminium powder. Alternatively, add some fluorescein to the water. Blow some smoke into the top half of the flask. Use a slide projector fitted with a narrow slit to project a beam of light into the flask. Aim the beam at the centre of the flask and move the projector slowly from position A to position B, (Fig. 211). Notice carefully what happens to the beam when the projector is in various positions.

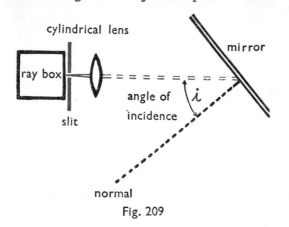

Fig. 209

When light passes from glass to air or from water to air, it may be partially refracted and partially reflected or it may be totally reflected, depending on the angle at which the light ray strikes the surface. What happens to the beam when it passes from the water to the air at an angle to the surface?

ease. As each fibre transmits light independently of the others, it is possible to 'see' through or take photographs through such a system. Many new applications of fibre optics are rapidly being found, particularly where it is required to take pictures in inaccessible places! (Fig. 212).

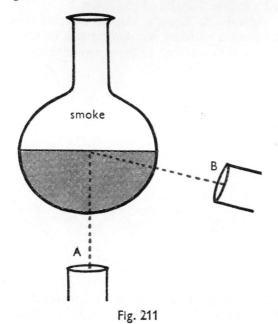

Fig. 211

Fig. 212

(b) As an alternative to the above experiment semicircular perspex blocks may be used in conjunction with ray boxes.

Experiment 7.8. Cover an egg with a layer of carbon by holding it in a candle flame. The carbon traps a layer of air round the egg which remains even if the egg is dropped into water. Can you explain why the egg appears to be silver when the egg is submerged in water?

The total internal reflection of light inside a perspex rod$_{16}$ permits light to be transmitted from one end to the other even when the rod is bent. This principle is used in some toy cars to supply light to their headlamps. The Corgi model of the Rover 2000 is one such example.

A recent development of this principle of total internal reflection is called *fibre optics.* Flexible bundles of many thousands of fine glass fibres transmit light round corners with

Experiment 7.9.

(a) Place a coin in a mug or can and move your head so that the coin is just out of your field of vision (Fig. 213). Without moving your eye pour water into the can. Can you now see the coin? Why?

(b) Observe a pencil placed in a beaker half full of water. Can you explain what you see?

Experiment 7.10. Lay a block of glass on a sheet of paper and project on to it a thin beam of light from a ray box, (Fig. 214). Rotate the block and see what happens to the ray as it passes into and out of the glass. Replace the glass block with a triangular prism. What do you see?

If two triangular and one rectangular glass prisms are arranged as shown in Fig. 215, three parallel rays of light can be made to converge to a point. A converging lens may be considered as a number of such prisms joined together.

Demonstration 7.11. *Focusing effect of a lens.* Fix a 100 watt clear electric lamp in a large can as shown. Place a piece of perforated hardboard (pegboard) one metre from it and a translucent screen beyond that. Hardboard with $\frac{7}{4}$ in holes drilled 1 in apart is suitable. A series of images of the filament will be produced on the screen. Each hole behaves like the pinhole in a pinhole camera. Are the images sharp or fuzzy? Why?

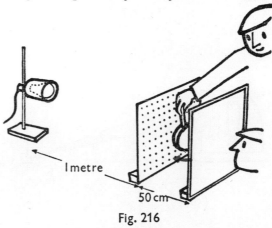

Fig. 216

Now place a large magnifying glass (e.g. f = 20 cm) between the screen and the hardboard, and slowly move the lens towards the hardboard. Many of the beams of light will then be seen to converge, and the images will almost coincide at one lens position.

Experiment 7.12.

(*a*) Study a selection of lenses and see if you can use them to project pictures (images) on a sheet of paper. What else can they be used for? A boy silhouetted against a window makes a good 'object', particularly if you ask him to wave his arms!

(*b*) Can you make a lens from a drop of water held in a tiny loop of wire?

From these experiments you will have discovered that light is bent when it passes into or out of glass or water. This bending is called *refraction*, and is caused by the fact that light travels more slowly in glass and water than in air. It is because light waves are slowed down when they enter a lens that focusing is possible.

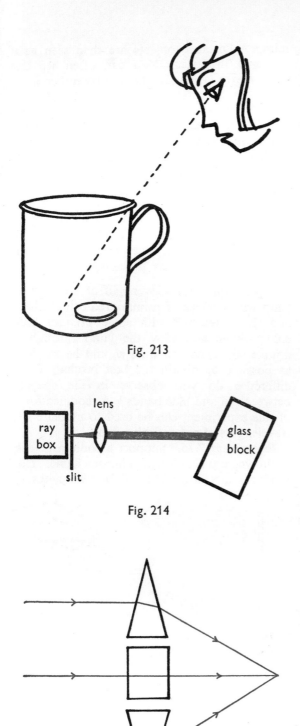

Fig. 213

Fig. 214

Fig. 215

The focusing action of a converging (convex) lens used in a camera and slide projector is illustrated in Figs. 217 and 218.

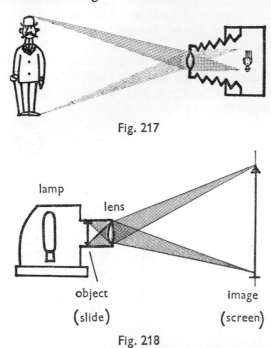

Fig. 217

Fig. 218

Demonstration 7.13. Pour a mixture of 59 per cent carbon tetrachloride and 41 per cent benzene into a measuring jar, and place a pyrex glass rod into the jar. It is possible to obtain a mixture in which the rod is invisible. Why is this?

Fig. 219

Light travels more quickly in less dense hot air than in cold air. Light rays are therefore bent as shown in Fig. 219, thus producing a mirage. Distance objects are then seen as if mirrored in water. You can often see this effect above tarmac roads in hot weather.

Diffraction

Diffraction effects were seen in the ripple tank. Similar effects are found to occur with light, but simple demonstrations cannot easily be explained at this stage.

Interference

The interference pattern produced by a double slit shows us that light is a wave motion. We can now use the same double slit to see if red and blue light have different wavelengths.

Experiment 7.14. Cover half of a showcase lamp with a piece of primary red colour filter, and the other half with some primary blue colour filter and view the lamp through a double slit. The two lines should be as close as possible to obtain the best results. What difference do you observe in the spacing between red and blue bands? A modified form of this experiment can be used to measure the wavelengths of red and blue light.

Experiment 7.15. Support a sodium pencil, as shown, and heat it with a bunsen flame. This produces a yellow light. Take two pieces of

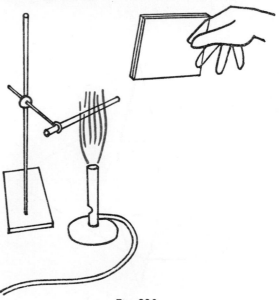

Fig. 220

ordinary window glass, press them together and look at the reflection of the flame in the sheets of glass. Such glass is sufficiently uneven to produce a series of air wedges between the sheets. What do you see?

Patterns of this kind are called Newton's rings, and can often be seen in the wedges produced between a colour slide and its glass

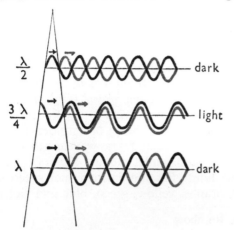

Fig. 221. Reflections at two surfaces of an air wedge.

mount. Special roughened glass is now available which prevents the formation of such rings

If light is reflected at both faces of a wedge of air the reflected waves may be in phase or out of phase. In Fig. 221 only the *reflected* waves are drawn. When the waves are in phase bright bands are produced and when they are out of phase they cancel to give dark bands. The air wedge may be formed between two sheets of glass touching at only one end. Bands or rings are formed if single colour (mono-chromatic) light is being used.

Velocity of light

About three hundred years ago a Danish astronomer called Roemer gave the first reasonably accurate value for the speed of light. He calculated it in a very ingenious way from a careful study of the eclipses of one of Jupiter's moons. It was some 200 years later before his results were confirmed by direct experiments conducted on the Earth.

A. A. Michelson, an American physicist, spent many years measuring the velocity of light. A simplified version of one of his methods is illustrated in Fig. 222. An octagonal mirror was used to reflect the light coming from a powerful arc lamp. The beam then passed to a mirror (M) situated 22 miles away on Mount San Antonio. From there the beam was reflected

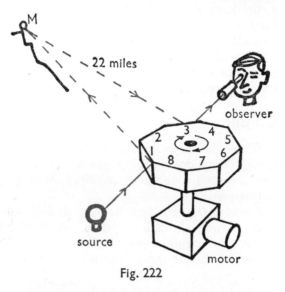

Fig. 222

back to the octagonal mirror and hence to the observer. The light therefore traveled 44 miles between the source and the observer.

If the octagonal mirror is stationary in the position shown, light will be reflected from the faces 1 and 3, and the observer will see the light. If the mirror rotates so that the faces are lying at any angle other than the one shown, no light will be reflected to M. Similarly, if light is coming from Mount San Antonio to the octagonal mirror it will not then be reflected towards the observer. Thus the observer can see the light only if, when the light falls on them, the faces of the octagonal mirror are in the positions shown.

Suppose now that the mirror is rotating so that light striking face 1 and mirror M travels the 44 miles and returns to the octagonal mirror by the time face 2 has moved to the original position of face 3. Then the observer will again see the light. To calculate the velocity of light the mirror is gradually speeded up from rest until the light is observed for the first time with the revolving mirror.

If the mirror were then found to be turning 530 times every second, what would you say was the speed of light in air? (16) Could light be observed at any other rate of rotation of the mirror? (17)

Measurements obtained from such experiments have shown that light travels at about 186,000 miles per second (3×10^8 metres per second) in air. Its speed is similar in space. The speed of light in water is about 140,000 miles per second and in glass about 120,000 miles per second.

Colour

Where do the colours in the rainbow come from? Why does a soap bubble or oil film produce such a range of colours? Why is a red ball red?

About 300 years ago Newton studied sunlight passing through a prism. A band of colours (spectrum) was obtained. You can conduct a similar experiment with a ray box.

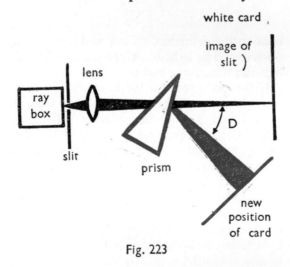

Fig. 223

Experiment 7.16. Fix a narrow slit in front of a ray box, and use a converging lens to produce an image of the slit on a white card (Fig. 223). Place a triangular glass prism between the lens and the card, as shown in red, and move the screen until a spectrum of colour is obtained. You should now rotate the prism

until a spectrum is produced with the screen as near to its original position as possible, that is, until the angle D (called the angle of deviation) is as small as possible. By rotating the card slightly you can spread out the band of colours. How many colours can you identify? Where have the colours come from? What does this tell you about white light?

When light rays pass from air to glass they slow down and are bent. *What is this bending called? (18)* Some rays are bent more than others. Those which are slowed down most will be bent most. *What colour of light travels most quickly through glass? (19) What colour travels most slowly? (20)*

The colour of a beam of light depends on its wavelength. Red has a wavelength of about 700 mμ and violet about 400 mμ. Between these limits lies the entire visual spectrum of red, orange, yellow, green, blue and violet.

The Rainbow

White light can be split up into its component colours as it passes through small transparent spheres such as raindrops. The light is refracted and reflected.

Demonstration 7.17.

You can see how a rainbow produces its spectrum of colours by studying this model (Fig. 224). Fill a spherical flask with water, and

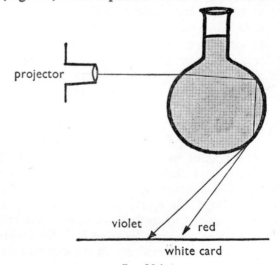

Fig. 224

add a few drops of liquid Lux and a very small quantity of fine aluminium powder to enable you to see the path of the beam through the water. Now make a very narrow slit by inserting two pieces of black paper in a slide holder and place the slide with the slit horizontal in a projector. Focus the projector to produce a clear image of this slit at the flask, and project a flat beam of light through the flask as shown in Fig. 224. A 'rainbow' can then be formed on a sheet of paper placed below the flask.

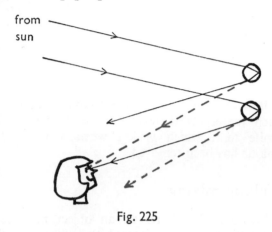

Fig. 225

You might think from Fig. 224 that the red part of a rainbow should be *below* the violet. This is not, however, what is normally seen. *Can you explain from Fig. 225 why the red part is uppermost? (21) Remember that a real rainbow is formed by thousands of tiny water drops.*

Experiment 7.18. A 'rainbow' can be produced artificially by sprinkling some polystyrene beads on a sheet of black paper and holding a torch or car bulb about a foot above it. Place a small cover over the bulb to reduce glare, and view this apparatus from above as shown in Fig. 226.

If you were in a high-flying aircraft, a rainbow would appear circular as did the bow formed round the car bulb. A line drawn from the centre of the rainbow to the sun would then pass through you. In practice, of course, a rainbow appears as a circular arc of light seen in the direction opposite to the sun. It is the

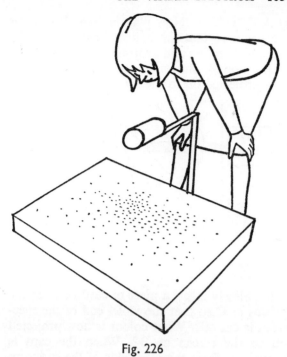

Fig. 226

raindrops only in this particular band that send back the spectrum colours to your eyes. Someone standing in a different place would see a spectrum produced by other water drops. Everyone, in fact, sees a different rainbow. The spray from a waterfall or garden hose can also produce rainbow effects.

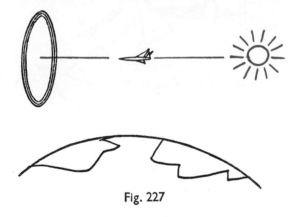

Fig. 227

Primary and Complementary Colours
Experiment 7.19.

(a) Set up the apparatus as in Experiment 7.16, and produce a spectrum on the screen at A (Fig. 228). Now place a second prism in the beam so that the light is bent back to its original direction and projected on to the screen in position B, shown in red. What colour is now projected on to the screen?

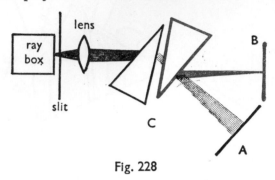

lens

ray box

slit

B

C

A

Fig. 228

(b) Slowly insert a piece of card between the prisms at C so that the violet end of the spectrum is cut off. What colour is now projected on to the screen at B? When the card is brought in from the other side of the spectrum so that the red end is cut off, what colour is left? The colour removed and the colour left are said to be complementary. Two complementary colours when added together produce white light.

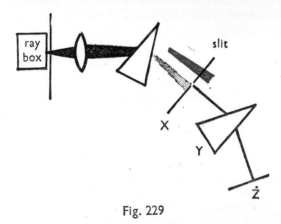

ray box

slit

X

Y

Z

Fig. 229

Experiment 7.20.

(a) Set up the apparatus as in Experiment 7.16 and produce a spectrum on the screen at X (Fig. 229). Now remove the screen and hold in its place a card containing a long narrow slit about 1 mm wide. Select one colour from the spectrum, and allow it to pass through the slit and then through another prism (Y) so that the ray is projected on to a screen at Z. Is the coloured beam split up into a further range of colours? Repeat this experiment with various colours in the spectrum.

(b) Return the screen to its original position A so that the apparatus is set up as it was for Experiment 7.16. Now insert a red filter between the lens and the prism, and note the result obtained. Repeat the experiment, using green and blue filters. Red, blue and green are chosen as the primary colours.

(c) Insert a turquoise filter between the lens and the prism, and observe the spectrum produced. Repeat the experiment with magenta and yellow filters. Turquoise, magenta and yellow are the complementary colours, that is, each represents the part of the spectrum of white light which is left when a primary colour has been removed.

Colour mixing

White light shining on an object may be reflected, absorbed or transmitted. A piece of black cloth absorbs practically all the light incident on it and so it appears black. Glass transmits most of the light and so appears colourless. Snow reflects all the light and appears white.

When white light shines on a blue object, the red, orange, yellow, green and violet colours present in white light are absorbed by the object, and the blue part of the spectrum is reflected. A colour filter absorbs some colours and allows others to pass through. A red filter, for example, absorbs the green and blue parts of the spectrum and allows red light to pass. For simplicity you can think of three cheap primary filters as each allowing about one-third of the spectrum to pass through.

R} A red filter absorbs all colours other than
O} red and orange

Y} A green filter absorbs all colours other than
G} yellow and green

B} A blue filter absorbs all colours other than
V} blue and violet

Adding Colours

Experiment 7.21. You can construct a simple colour mixing box from a 1 lb syrup tin, a 12 volt 24 watt car bulb and some colour filters. Cut 3 slits, about 2 in. × ¼ in., in the tin and fix a bulb holder to the lid. The bulb filament should be opposite the middle of each slit. Fix pieces of primary red, green and blue colour filter over the slits, using rubber bands. By placing a plane mirror at either side of the can, the three beams of light can be directed on to a white screen.

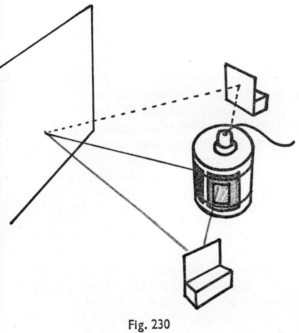

Fig. 230

Use the colour box to investigate the colours produced when you add green and blue, green and red, then blue and red. What colour is produced by *adding* all three primary colours? You can adjust the amount of coloured light falling on the screen by moving the mirrors further from the slits.

Colour mixing apparatus is available commercially[18].

Subtracting Colours

Each of the complementary colour filters allows about two thirds of the spectrum to pass through. The yellow filter, for example, allows all the colours except blue and violet to pass.

Turquoise = white − red = blue + green
Magenta = white − green = blue + red
Yellow = white − blue = green + red

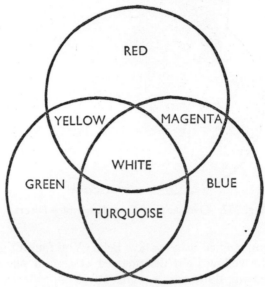

Fig. 231. Overlapping Beams of Light.

Experiment 7.22. Hold a piece of yellow and a piece of magenta colour filter so that they overlap, and look through them at a source of white light. What colour do you see? The yellow filter absorbs the blue, and the magenta absorbs the green parts of the spectrum, leaving only the red to pass.

Repeat this experiment, with magenta and turquoise filters and then with yellow and turquoise filters. What happens if all three filters are placed together?

Filters and paints absorb certain colours and reflect others. If two paints are mixed, only colours which *both* paints originally reflected will now be reflected. Turquoise and yellow both reflect green and therefore turquoise and yellow paints will combine to give green.

Colours produced by interference

(a) Wedges

Light reflected from both sides of a thin wedge produces interference patterns, which

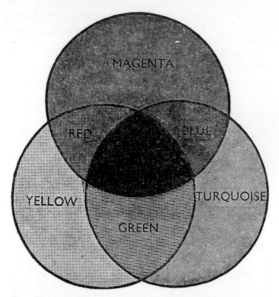

Fig. 232. Overlapping Complementary Filters.

you studied using yellow light. You found that the yellow light disappeared at certain places leaving dark bands. This effect happens with all the colours of the spectrum, but the dark bands for each colour appear at different places. If the wedge is illuminated with white light a series of coloured bands is produced. Where you see (say) a turquoise band the thickness of the wedge is such that the red light has been removed from the spectrum.

(b) Diffraction gratings

The interference effects of a large number of very narrow slits—several thousand per centimetre—may be used to produce a colour spectrum. The arrangement is called a *diffraction grating*[29, 53] and is often used in place of a prism in spectrometers and spectroscopes.

Emission and absorption spectra

To study the range of colour (spectrum) produced by a source of light we use a spectrometer (Fig. 233). This is really a refined version of the apparatus you used to examine the light from a tungsten bulb. A narrow slit is illuminated by the source and the image of the slit

seen through the prism is examined by the aid of a telescope.

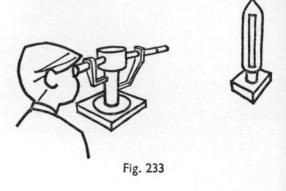

Fig. 233

Demonstration 7.23. Use a spectroscope or spectrometer to study the spectra produced by a sodium flame, a mercury vapour lamp[2,4], and any gas filled discharge tubes available. How do the spectra produced by these sources differ from the spectrum of a tungsten filament lamp?

We have already seen that light is emitted when an electron jumps from one energy level to another in an atom. The energy levels in the atoms of different elements are not the same, so that the light emitted by an atom of a particular element enables us to recognise the element from which it came. This emission spectrum is often used as a kind of atomic fingerprint to help scientists identify an element. One thirty-thousand-millionth of a gram of sodium can be detected in this way.

If white light is passed through the vapour of an element, the atoms absorb energy at exactly the same wavelengths as the light radiated by the same atoms when they are in an excited state. If the white light is then passed through a spectrometer and examined, *dark* bands are found in exactly the same positions as the *bright* bands of the emission spectrum.

Demonstration 7.24. Use a sodium stick to produce a sodium flame, and study its spectrum in a spectrometer. Now project a powerful beam of white light through the flame and into the spectrometer. A 750 watt slide projector will provide enough light for this experiment.

If the flame is not too bright dark bands can be observed. This is called an absorption spectrum.

The examination of absorption spectra produced by gaseous elements of the sun enabled scientists to discover an element in the sun before it had been discovered on Earth. They called it helium after the Greek name for the sun, Helios.

Seeing colour

Our perception of colour results from a complicated process in which the wavelength of the light itself is only one factor. Some of the colours we see have no single wavelength. They are produced by a mixture of different wavelengths. Browns and purples come into this category. Other colours such as yellow may be perceived when the eye admits light of a single wavelength (for example, from a sodium source) or a mixture of red and green light.

Our minds interpret the image produced on the retina of the eye in terms of our past experience. *Describe some of the optical illusions you have seen which result from such 'interpretations'* (22)

Normally we observe colours illuminated by sunlight, which is white light. Consequently we have become accustomed to accepting as *white* the light by which we see things, even if it is coloured. For example we perceive white paper as *white* when it is illuminated by an electric bulb producing yellow light. This is true, of course, only within certain limits, and no one would claim that a sodium street lamp produced white light. Nevertheless even sodium lamps can produce light which we eventually accept as white under certain conditions. If snow-covered streets are illuminated by sodium lamps, you can observe fascinating colour changes if the snow is suddenly illuminated by the much *whiter* light from a car headlamp.

In the following demonstration you will see to what extent background illumination is *unconsciously* taken to be *white* even though you may consciously perceive it as coloured!

Demonstration 7.25. For this experiment you will require two 35 mm projectors and two slides. Stick narrow strips of black paper on the slides, and place them in the projectors to produce crosses as shown in Fig. 234. The cross produced by projector No. 2 is coloured red *on the diagram* for ease of identification. Both crosses are, of course, produced by the absence of light. They are both therefore black.

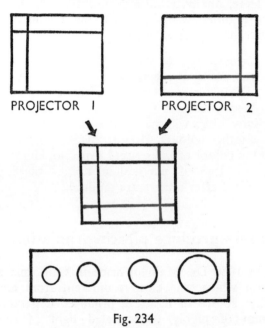

Fig. 234

Move the projectors so that the two projected patterns overlap as shown. The 'red' cross is receiving *no light* from projector No. 2. It is therefore illuminated only by projector No. 1.

Now place a blue filter over the front of the lens of projector No. 2. What is the background colour now? What colour does the 'red' cross appear to be? What colour of light is actually falling on the 'red' cross?

To obtain the best results it may be necessary to reduce the amount of light coming from projector No. 1. This may be done by sliding over the lens a card in which holes of various sizes have been cut (Fig. 234).

Repeat this experiment, using different colour filters in front of projector No. 2. Can you discover a relationship between the background colour and the colour of the 'red' cross?

The last experiment showed that colour vision is not dependent only on the wavelength of the light entering the eyes. It depends, in addition, on the mind (psychological factors) and on the structure of the eye itself (physiological factors). Statistics suggest that between 5–10 per cent of men are at least partially colour blind, whereas less than 1 per cent of women have this defect.

Here, finally, is an experiment which shows yet another way in which the colour you perceive may be affected.

Experiment 7.26. Gaze for a minute or so at one point on a brightly coloured object and then transfer your gaze to a blank wall. Try to keep your eyes relaxed, that is, focused on infinity. You will see an 'after image' produced in another colour. How is this colour related to the colour of the object? After looking at a small piece of magnesium ribbon burning, excellent after images are produced.

Lasers produce piercing radiation

In 1960 Dr. Maiman made in California a lamp which was entirely different from any other source of light. It produced a parallel beam of highly concentrated light of one particular wavelength (694 mμ). This beam had the amazing property of spreading out only very very slightly no matter how far it travelled. Such rays can transmit sufficient power to melt metals and can bore through a stack of razor blades.

If you could study in great detail the light waves coming from an ordinary source you would find that they were irregular. In contrast, the waves from a radio transmitter are perfectly regular. Consider the difference between a crowd coming from a football match and a highly trained regiment marching in step all the way. As the excited atoms, which produce light in a normal source, emit their radiations in a random fashion, there is no regularity about the waves produced. Dr. Maiman's new source, the *laser*, produced orderly light waves which were 'in step'.

Laser beams can carry information through space, losing practically none of their strength on the way. A beam reflected from the moon, for example, can be detected on Earth. New uses are continually being found for lasers in communication, astronomy, medicine and industry.

How is light detected?

Light waves may be detected in many ways. When light falls on certain substances, such as photographic emulsion, chemical changes take place. A photograph is really a record of the total amount of light energy that has fallen on the different parts of the film. 'Developing' continues the chemical action begun by the light.

Light energy may be transformed to electrical energy by using a photo-voltaic cell. The current produced then operates a micro-ammeter, which gives an indication of how well the cell is illuminated. A photographic exposure meter is such a device. It indicates *illumination*.

The electrical resistance of certain materials such as cadmium-sulphide varies with the amount of light falling on them. Photo-resistors of this kind are used to control the light entering automatic cameras and also to operate light-sensitive switches.

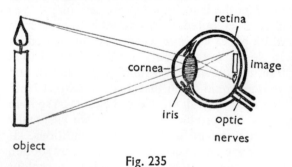

Fig. 235

The Eye

The human eye is the most remarkable light detector of all. In some ways it resembles a camera. The retina of the eye takes the place of the film in the camera. It consists of millions of tiny nerve endings, called *rods* and *cones*, which respond to the light falling on them. The rods are mainly concerned with the strength of the light and the cones with its colour. The information from the rods and cones is then transmitted through the optic nerve to the brain.

Unlike the hard lens of the camera, the lens in the eye is altered in shape each time we focus our eyes. If the lens were solid, it would have to pop out like an organ stop every time we focused on something close at hand!

The amount of light entering our eyes is controlled by the iris which alters the size of the central opening (pupil). The transparent outer case of the eye is called the cornea, (Fig. 235).

Binocular Vision –

We estimate distances, both by focusing our eyes, and by making them rotate in their sockets, (Fig. 236). The following experiment shows how much we depend on this rotation of both eyes when we are judging distances.

Fig. 237

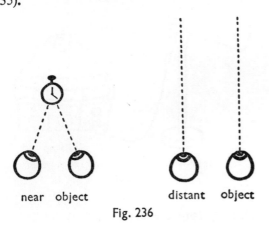

near object   distant   object

Fig. 236

Experiment 7.27. Hold two long pencils at an arm's length as shown in Fig. 237. With one eye closed bring them together so that the points of the pencils touch. Repeat this operation with both eyes open.

Visual aids

Infra-red radiation

CHAPTER 8

When electro-magnetic waves are absorbed by an object, their energy is transformed into heat, that is, the molecules of the object are speeded up. Sir William Herschel discovered in 1800 that thermometers placed in a spectrum produced by the sun's rays registered more heat beyond the red end of the visible spectrum than within it. Most thermal radiation comes from the region beyond the red part of the spectrum. It is called *infra-red radiation*. This radiation is sometimes called 'radiant heat'. The source emits energy in the form of electro-magnetic waves. This energy appears as heat only when the radiation is absorbed by a body whose molecules are excited into more rapid motion.

How are infra-red waves produced?

An electric radiator, a gas fire and a glowing coal fire all produce infra-red radiation. A soldering iron and a smoothing iron also produce infra-red radiation without glowing. The higher the temperature of the body the greater is the amount of radiant energy emitted. The heat we receive from the sun travels across space as electro-magnetic waves.

How can we detect infra-red waves?

The simplest way to detect infra-red radiation is to allow it to strike your hand. If the radiation is strong enough it will produce a sensation of heat. *Can you suggest two disadvantages of this method of detection for scientific work? (1)*

To overcome these disadvantages various instruments have been devised.

Thermopile

When two different metals are joined together and heated what happens? (2) What is this device called? (3) A series of such junctions are connected together, and the output is fed to a sensitive micro-ammeter, which registers when infra-red radiation falls on the junctions. A horn is sometimes fitted round the thermopile to collect radiation from one direction.

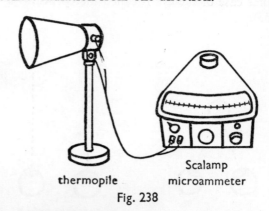

thermopile

Scalamp microammeter

Fig. 238

Black Bulb Thermometer

A flask covered with matt black paint may be used as an infra-red detector. The air-filled flask is connected to a length of glass tubing in either of the two ways indicated in Fig. 239. *Can you explain what happens in each case when infra-red rays strike the flask? (4)*

Bolometer

The electrical resistance of a metal depends on its temperature. One form of bolometer uses the change in resistance of platinum wire when infra-red rays strike it to indicate the strength of the radiation.

Photo-Transistor

A Mullard OCP71 wired in the circuit shown[4,7] (Fig. 240 (a)) will act as an excellent detector of infra-red radiation. The photo-transistor is perhaps the simplest sensitive

110

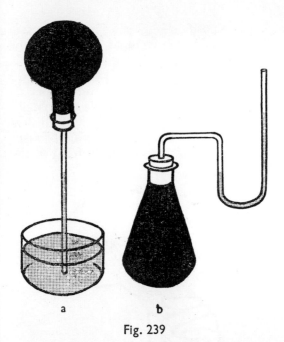

Fig. 239

infra-red detector for school use. It is used in the following experiment to indicate how the infra-red radiation from a source changes as the temperature rises.

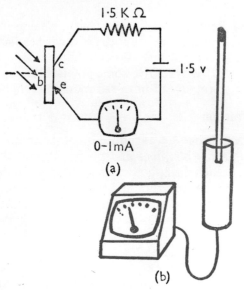

(a)

(b)

Fig. 240

Experiment 8.1. Connect an electric heater to the output terminals of a rotary transformer[30]. Place an infra-red detector about

30 cm away from the heater as shown in Fig. 241. Now gradually increase the voltage supplied to the heater, thus raising its temperature. What effect has this on the meter reading?

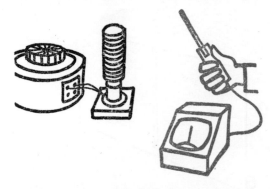

Fig. 241

Photographic Film

In addition to the above instruments special photographic films may be used to detect infra-red radiation. Photographs can be taken in darkness by using infra-red rays. Such photographs often show details not recorded by light-sensitive films.

How are infra-red rays transmitted?

Infra-red rays from the sun travel through empty space. An electric lamp may be evacuated yet your hand will be warmed if placed near it. As with light, infra-red rays will travel through a vacuum.

When a cloud moves in front of the sun, the light and the infra-red rays are partially cut off at the same time. A similar result is observed during an eclipse. *What does this tell you about the speed of light waves and infra-red waves? (5) Does it suggest that they have any other properties in common? (6)*

Straight Line Propagation

Experiment 8.2. Place two 18 in square asbestos boards half an inch apart in front of an electric heater so that the rays pass through the gap as shown in Fig. 242. Use a photo transistor to discover where infra-red rays can be detected. Do your results suggest that infra-red rays travel in straight lines?

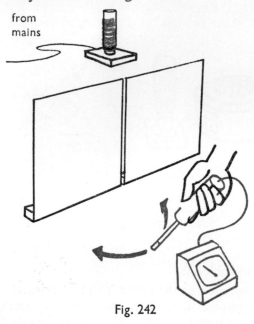

from mains

Fig. 242

Reflection

Experiment 8.3.

(a) Place an infra-red lamp at one side and an infra-red detector at the other side of an asbestos sheet. Now bring up a polished metal

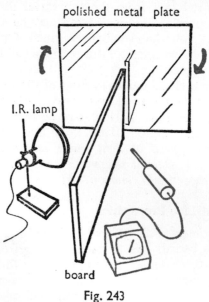

polished metal plate

I.R. lamp

board

Fig. 243

plate to the position shown in Fig. 243; rotate it slightly, noting the readings on the detector meter. At what position of the metal plate is the greatest amount of radiation detected? What does this suggest? Use other materials as reflectors and report the results you obtain. To test whether or not it is visible light which is activating the detector, place a one-foot-square sheet of No. 87 infra-red filter[35] in front of the lamp.

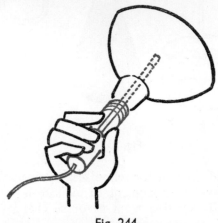

Fig. 244

(b) Repeat this experiment, placing the photo-transistor at the focus of a car headlamp reflector (Fig. 244). What difference do you observe? Why? Give some practical examples of this property of infra-red radiation.

Refraction

Experiment 8.4. Produce a colour spectrum using a ray box, lens and prism. Prisms filled with carbon disulphide are particularly suitable. Explore the spectrum and the regions on either side of it with a photo-transistor, (Fig. 245). Where does the detector register the highest reading? Have the infra-red rays been bent as they passed through the prism?

Demonstration 8.5. Fill a flask with a concentrated solution of iodine in carbon tetrachloride so that practically no visible rays pass through it. Set up an infra-red bulb at one end of the laboratory and the flask at the other. Hold the photo-transistor in front of the flask and see if you can detect any infra-red rays.

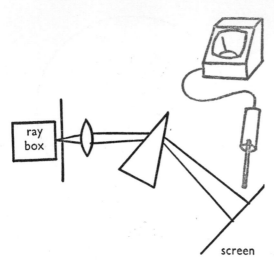

Fig. 245

Now place the detector behind the flask as shown in Fig. 246. Move it around slowly whilst watching the meter reading. Can you explain the results you obtain?

Fig. 246

Experiment 8.6. Sit in front of a gas or electric fire so that you can feel the heat on your face. Now place a sheet of clear glass between the fire and your face. What does the result tell you about the glass?

Only the infra-red rays near the visible spectrum pass through the glass; the longer infra-red rays are absorbed by it. A greenhouse allows the shorter waves to pass through and heat the soil which, in turn, re-radiates long wave infra-red rays. As glass is opaque to these rays the heat is 'trapped'.

Water is also opaque to the longer infra-red rays. The water vapour in the Earth's atmosphere allows the shorter infra-red rays from the sun to pass through, thus heating the Earth. On a clear night the Earth re-radiates long wave infra-red rays into space without hindrance. The Earth, therefore, cools down rapidly. Sharp frosts are common under such conditions. On a cloudy night the long infra-red rays are partially reflected to the Earth and partially absorbed by the clouds. Some of the absorbed radiation is re-radiated to the Earth, so that the cloud blanket traps the heat on the Earth's surface, as does the glass in a greenhouse.

Emission and absorption

As the temperature of a gas or electric heater rises, the radiation increases. This can be directly observed as a sensation of warmth. If, however, two different surfaces are at the same temperature, do they both radiate equally?

Experiment 8.7. Paint the outside of a can or calorimeter matt black, and polish the outside of another similar calorimeter. Place the calorimeters on corks and pour 100 cm³ of hot water into each calorimeter. Fit corks and thermometers in each as shown in Fig. 247,

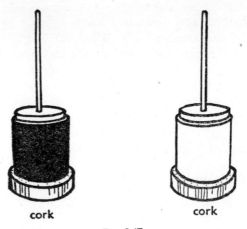

cork   cork

Fig. 247

and check that the two temperatures are the same. Why should the calorimeters be corked? Why were the calorimeters placed on corks?

Read the two temperatures after 15 minutes and state what you conclude from your results.

Experiment 8.8. The apparatus used in the last experiment may be used to compare the absorption of heat by dark and bright surfaces.

Fig. 249

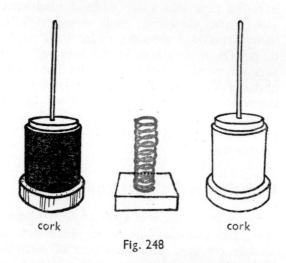

cork   cork

Fig. 248

Pour 100 cm³ of cold water into each calorimeter and check the temperatures. Place an electric heater about 20 cm from each calorimeter and note the water temperature after the heater has been on for 15 minutes. Which is the better absorber of infra-red rays? Is the better radiator also a better absorber?

Is it an advantage or a disadvantage for kettles, saucepans and vacuum flasks to have bright exteriors? (7) Why? (8) Explain why on a sunny day a dark brown leaf lying on top of snow may gradually sink down into the snow. (9)

Can you discover what a radiometer is and how it works? (10) (Fig. 249). Remember that the gas molecules in contact with a vane will be heated if the surface of the vane is hot.

Obliquity

Infra-red waves and light waves behave similarly. For most practical purposes both can be assumed to travel in straight lines, and the amount of radiation falling on each square centimetre of surface is greatest when the surface is at right angles to the direction in which the rays are moving. *Why is it warmer at the equator than at the poles? (11)* (See Book 1, page 23.)

Uses of infra-red radiation

Infra-red rays make the atoms and molecules of a substance vibrate. By discovering the frequencies to which a substance responds, much has been discovered about the structure and the nature of chemical bonds. Infra-red spectroscopy has grown into an important branch of chemical analysis.

Infra-red lamps are used in industry for many processes. Paints and enamels are dried and baked by such lamps. Shoemakers use them to activate the cement holding a worn sole to the rest of the shoe. In this way the sole can be easily removed. To accelerate the growth of chickens, they are reared under infra-red lamps.

During the 1939–45 war infra-red lamps were fitted to military vehicles for night driving. Using an image converter (nicknamed the 'snooperscope') which changed the invisible scene into a visible picture, the driver was able to see the road in front of him. An enemy, not equipped with such apparatus, could not see the vehicle.

In countries where the sun shines regularly its rays are concentrated by large curved mirrors and used to cook food. Portable solar cookers, rather like umbrellas, may be used for picnics. (See Book 1, page 126.)

Visual aids

16 mm Sound Films
   20.4735 Heat Rays[44]

Electron pumps

CHAPTER 9

Flow of charge

We are forever using familiar things as illustrations or models to describe the way less familiar things behave. For example, we are using a model if we speak of light *waves*. We mean by this description that light behaves in a similar way to the waves with which we are familiar, such as those on the surface of water. *What particular property of light do we use as a test of its wave nature? (1)*

Electric charges moving through solids, liquids and gases behave in some ways rather like fluids moving through tubes or like heat passing along a metal bar. For this reason we have referred to this movement of charge as a *flow*. Georg Simon Ohm studied the flow of heat through metal, and wondered if it might be similar in any way to the flow of electricity through a conductor. To find an answer he devised experiments which led to his discovery of the famous law which now bears his name. Remember, however, that when we refer to the movement of electric charge as a flow we are using an analogy and that there are many ways in which the movement does not resemble other types of flow.

The following demonstrations will remind you of the conditions necessary for flow to occur.

Demonstration 9.1.

(a) Water flows between the two jars in Fig. 250 because of the pressure difference. When does the water stop flowing?

(b) Air flows from the inflated football bladder to the other because of the difference in air pressure.

(c) Heat flows through a copper bar joining a can of hot water to a can of cold water or ice because there is a temperature difference.

(d) Electrons flow from a negatively charged electroscope to an uncharged one when a conductor connects them. This is due to the potential difference. When does the charge stop flowing?

If one electroscope were charged positively and the other were discharged what would happen when they were connected?

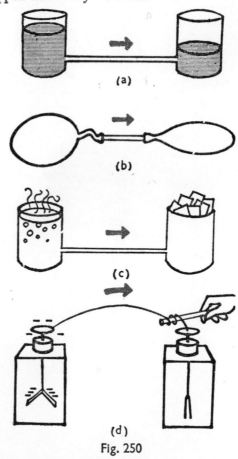

Fig. 250

In liquids and gases and in some solids both positive and negative charges move. We will indicate the movement of positive charges by

116

red arrows, and the movement of negative charges (electrons) by black arrows. In many cases it is enough to know that a current is flowing, and its direction does not matter in the least. We must, however, have some way of distinguishing direction when we come to discuss the magnetic effect of current. In metals, such as copper, an electric current consists of movement of negative charges, so that we will be using black arrows to indicate *electron flow* in such conductors. When electrons flow at a rate of 6×10^{18} electrons per second we call this a current of one ampere (1 amp). We will see later that the ampere is measured by an effect produced when this *quantity* of electricity passes every second.

As some text-books still use the old convention which shows current direction as the (often imaginary) movement of positive charges, you should always find out if the arrows indicate *electron flow* or *conventional current* when referring to such books.

Cause and effect

Cause

In order that an electric current may flow between two points two conditions are necessary. First there must be a difference of potential (voltage) between the points, and secondly the points must be connected by an electrical conductor. *Name some good conductors.* (2)

Can you describe three ways which you have already used to produce a potential difference? (3) You detected this p.d. by noting that it produced a current in a conductor. One

method uses chemicals, one heat and the other a moving wire. These are usually described as chemical, thermal and magnetic methods of producing an electric current. Here are some other ways of producing a current.

Experiment 9.2.

(*a*) Allow light to fall on a photo-voltaic cell such as that used in a photographic exposure meter. What is used to indicate current in such an instrument?

(*b*) A small electric motor driven by solar cells[20] is illustrated in Fig. 251. This may be operated by sunlight or an ordinary electric bulb.

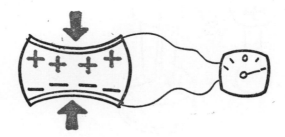

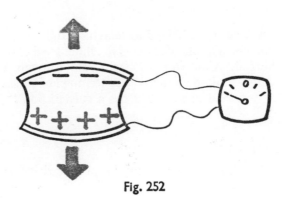

Fig. 252

Experiment 9.3. Connect a Pye Scalamp (7891/S) or similar sensitive micro-ammeter to a small crystal microphone insert. Squeeze the crystal and note the deflection in the meter. When such plates are subjected to pressures, voltages appear across them as shown in Fig. 252. This is referred to as the piezo-electric effect.

Fig. 251

Demonstration 9.4. For this experiment a volunteer with dry hair is required! Ask him to stand on a polythene basin and touch the dome of a Van de Graaff machine. Why does his hair stand on end when the machine is switched on?

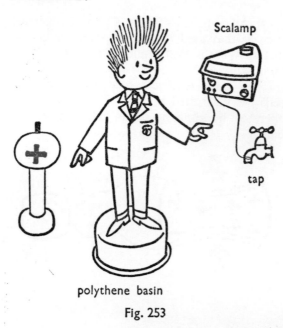

Scalamp

tap

polythene basin

Fig. 253

Ask your (ex-)friend to take his hand off the Van de Graaff dome. He should still be charged. Can you discharge him through a sensitive micro-ammeter, one terminal of which is connected to earth? Does a current flow?

Summary

An electric current may be produced in the following ways.

1. *By chemicals,* as in dry cells and car batteries.
2. *By heat,* as in the case of a thermocouple.
3. *By moving a wire in a magnetic field.* Dynamos use this principle.
4. *By light* shining on a photo-voltaic cell such as is used in an exposure meter. Artificial satellites are equipped with solar batteries which use a type of photo cell.
5. *By varying the pressure* applied to a crystal such as is used in a microphone or gramophone pick up.
6. *By friction.* A body can be charged by friction and allowed to discharge, thus causing an electric current to flow.

Effect

Once an electric current has been produced what effects does it have? *When ions flow through an electrolyte such as a salt solution, what happens? (4) State one practical use of such electrolysis. (5)* Metals are deposited on the negative plate (cathode) and a layer of metal can be removed from the positive plate (anode). The first effect is used in electro-plating and the second in electro-chemical shaping (machining) of metal surfaces. In the latter, a metal object such as an aerofoil section or a turbine blade, may be accurately machined. We refer to electrolysis as a *chemical effect* of an electric current.

When an electric current flows through the filament of a bulb or the element of an electric fire, what happens? (6) We refer to this as the *heating effect* of a current.

When a current passes through a coil of wire wound round a piece of iron, what happens to the iron? (7) We refer to this as the *magnetic effect.* When the iron is magnetised its length may alter slightly.

When an electric current flows through certain gases such as neon, sodium vapour and mercury vapour, the atoms are excited to radiate light energy. *Give examples of the practical use that is made of this fact. (8)* Some substances, such as zinc sulphide, will emit light when placed in an alternating electric field. Thin illuminating panels can thus be constructed. This form of lighting is called *electro-luminescence.*

When an electric potential is applied across certain crystals and ceramic materials they exert a mechanical force (*piezo-electric effect*). If an alternating voltage is used the substance will vibrate. Ultrasonic waves may be generated by such devices. A ceramic ultrasonic transducer, type 1404_{21}, may be used to transmit and to receive ultrasonic waves. It is particularly suitable for the remote control of equipment.

Summary

The main effects of an electric current can be summarised as follows.

1. *Chemical effect*, such as occurs during electrolysis. Electro-plating depends on this effect.
2. *Thermal effect*, which is used in electric heaters and tungsten filament lamps.
3. *Magnetic effect*, which is used to operate electric bells, relays and electric motors.
4. *Optical effects.* Many of our streets are lit by discharge tubes in which the atoms are electrically excited.
5. *Mechanical effects.* Mechanical vibrations are produced in certain crystals and ceramic materials by alternating currents. The frequencies of some radio transmitters are controlled by such vibrating crystals.

Visual aids

16 mm Sound Films
21.7488 What is Electric Current?[44]

Putting Free Electrons to Work[49]
Electricity and Light[49]

A vicious circle

CHAPTER 10

Conductors and insulators

An electric current will flow between two points only when a potential difference exists between them. Moreover there must be a conducting path between these two points. If there is a complete path round which electric charges can move, the arrangement is called an electric circuit.

Although all substances allow electricity to flow through them to some extent, we usually label materials *conductors* or *insulators*. A good conductor has a low resistance and a good insulator has a high resistance. Copper is a good conductor, and under similar circumstances about 10^{23} times as much current will flow through it as would flow through a piece of polythene of the same dimensions. Another way of expressing this difference is to say that 1 cm of polythene has about the same resistance as 100,000 light years of copper with the same cross-section! We therefore call polythene an insulator.

In the atoms of conductors the outer-shell electrons are loosely attached to the nucleus, and are referred to as *free electrons*. They are free to move between the atoms and normally do so in a random fashion.

Fig. 254

When a voltage is applied across the ends of a conductor (Fig. 254), there is, in addition to the random movement of electrons, a slow drift of electrons towards the positive end.

This electron movement is what we call electric current.

In the atoms of insulators the outer shell electrons are strongly attached to the nucleus, and electron movement between the atoms is much more difficult. Semi-conductors lie between these two extremes, and have peculiar properties which we will discuss later in the course.

You have already seen that, as the temperature rises, the resistance of some materials increases while the resistance of others decreases (Book 1, p. 86). *What happens to the resistance of iron wire when it is heated?* (*1*) In the following experiment you can watch a good insulator (glass) becoming a good conductor when it is heated.

Demonstration 10.1. Push two steel knitting needles through a large cork so that they are 1 in apart. Connect the needles in series with a 150 watt mains bulb as shown in Fig. 255. Now place a short length of $\frac{3}{16}$ in diameter soda glass rod across the needles and heat it with a bunsen burner. As soon as the bulb starts to glow remove the bunsen burner and watch!

Does the glass conduct electricity *before* it melts? The process of sealing the front on to T.V. tubes utilises this conducting property of hot glass.

Experiment 10.2. Resistance. Use a variable resistance (rheostat) in the circuit shown in Fig. 256 to control the current. What happens to the current, as indicated by the brightness of the bulb, when more resistance is put into the circuit? Now reverse the battery connections, so that the electrons move in the opposite direction. Does the direction of current flow affect the brightness of the bulb (heating effect)?

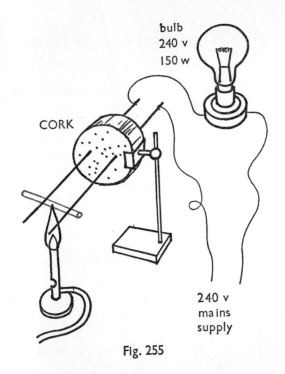

bulb
240 v
150 w

CORK

240 v
mains
supply

Fig. 255

Suitable cell-holders₂ and electrical compo-
nents₆ are available commercially.

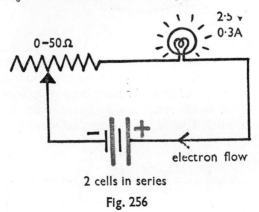

2·5 v
0·3A

0–50 Ω

electron flow

2 cells in series

Fig. 256

A mathematical reminder

Two quantities may be related in several
different ways. The cost of eggs, for example,
varies directly with the quantity purchased.
If 1 dozen eggs cost 4/-, 2 dozen will cost 8/-,
3 dozen 12/- and so on. We say the cost is
directly proportional to the quantity.

The mass of water is directly proportional to
the volume. If 1 cm³ has a mass of 1 g, 2 cm³

will have a mass of 2 g, 3 cm³ 3 g and so on.
We could construct a graph as shown in Fig.
257.

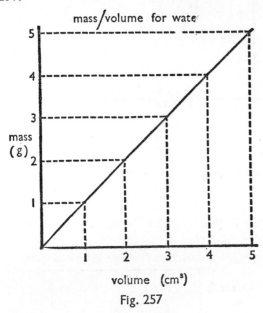

mass/volume for water

mass
(g)

volume (cm³)

Fig. 257

Notice that $\dfrac{\text{mass}}{\text{volume}} = \dfrac{1}{1} = \dfrac{2}{2} = \dfrac{3}{3} = \dfrac{4}{4}$ etc.

that is $\dfrac{\text{mass}}{\text{volume}} = \dfrac{M}{V} =$ a constant.

What is this particular constant called? (2)
Note. When two quantities are directly proportional

(a) they may be represented by a straight line
graph *which goes through the origin* and
(b) their ratio (that is one divided by the
other) is constant.

Ohm's law

Experiment 10.3. Connect a 1·5 volt dry cell
to a milliammeter (for example 0–1 mA), a
resistance (6 KΩ, ¼ watt) and a switch as
shown in Fig. 258. Close the switch and read
the current.

Now double the voltage applied to the circuit,
by connecting two cells in series. What assumption are we making here? Again read the

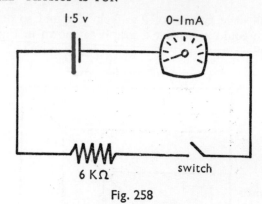

Fig. 258

current flowing in the circuit. Repeat this procedure with three and then four cells in series, and plot your results directly on to a graph as you do the experiment.

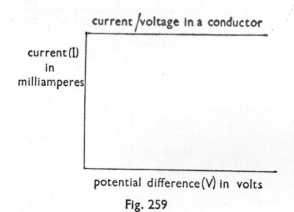

Fig. 259

How does the current vary with the voltage applied? Complete the table of results shown, expressing the current in amperes (not milliamperes), and finally calculate $\frac{V}{I}$ for each case.

Potential difference (V) in volts	1·5	3	4·5	6
current (I) in amperes				
$\frac{V}{I}$				

Fig. 260

What do you notice about the values of $\frac{V}{I}$ which you have just calculated? What does this tell you? What is the average value of $\frac{V}{I}$ when V is in volts and I in amperes?

You will often use the results of the last experiment in a later section of the course. The relationship you have found is called Ohm's Law and holds good for most, but not all, conductors kept at a constant temperature. The constant, which you obtained by dividing the voltage by the current, is called the *resistance* of the circuit. The unit of resistance is the *ohm*. The element of a one bar electric fire has a resistance of about 60 ohms. Ordinary lighting flex has a resistance of about 1/100th of an ohm per metre.

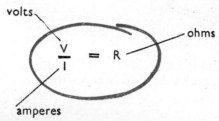

It is usual to use the letter V for voltage and I for current. C is not used as it is reserved for capacitance, a term with which we will deal later in the course. R represents resistance.

What is the resistance of a torch bulb which passes 0·3 A when 3·5 V is applied to it? (3)

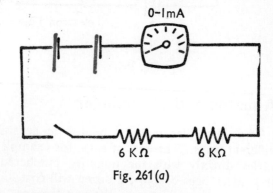

Fig. 261 (a)

Experiment 10.4.

(a) Using two cells in series, wire up the circuit as shown in Fig. 261(a). How does the current flowing in this circuit compare with the current which flowed when only one resistor was used? Assuming each cell has a voltage of 1·5 volt, find from the meter reading the total resistance when two such resistors are connected in series. You can assume that the rest of the circuit has a negligible resistance.

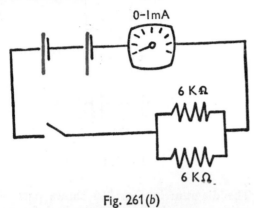
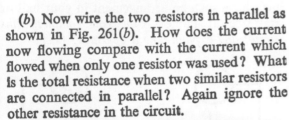

Fig. 261(b)

Fig. 262

(b) Now wire the two resistors in parallel as shown in Fig. 261(b). How does the current now flowing compare with the current which flowed when only one resistor was used? What is the total resistance when two similar resistors are connected in parallel? Again ignore the other resistance in the circuit.

Experiment 10.5. In this experiment you can find out if your body is a conductor or an insulator. Connect a sensitive micro-ammeter to a dry cell as shown in Fig. 262, and hold the ends of the wires with your fingers dry. Is there a meter reading? Repeat the experiment with your fingers wet. What difference do you observe? Is the greatest resistance to the flow of electricity inside your body or on the surface? Give a reason for your answer.

It is the strength of the current through your body which determines the 'shock' you receive.
Why is it dangerous to touch a mains circuit?
(4) Why is it even more dangerous, and often fatal, to do so with wet hands? (5)
If the current through your body is 150 μA (that is, 0·00015 A) when 1·5 V is applied, what is the resistance of your body? (6)

Series and parallel connections

Experiment 10.6. For the following experiments you will require two 1·5 volt dry cells and holders, two 2·5 volt 0·3 amp torch bulbs

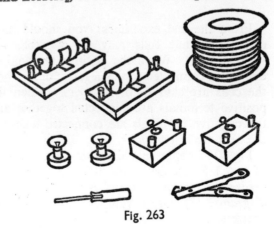

Fig. 263

and holders, two switches, some solid-core single p.v.c. wire, a screwdriver and a Bib wire stripper. One-foot lengths of wire are convenient.

We will assume that when *one* bulb is connected to *one* cell the brightness of the bulb is X units. You are asked to wire up various circuits so that each bulb has the same brightness (X), is appreciably brighter (>X) or is less bright (<X) as indicated in the following table. Once your circuit has been checked you should draw a diagram showing how the components are arranged. One word of warning; never connect a switch across the terminals of a cell, that is, never short circuit the cell. Why not?

	bulbs	cells	switches	brightness	comment
1.	1	1	–	X	–
2.	1	2	–	>X	–
3.	1	2	–	X	–
4.	1	1	1	X	–
5.	1	2	1	>X	–
6.	2	1	1	X	both bulbs switched
7.	2	1	1	<X	„ „ „
8.	2	2	1	X	„ „ „
9.	2	2	1	>X	„ „ „
10.	2	2	1	<X	„ „ „
11.	2	2	1	>X	only one bulb switched
12.	2	2	2	X	bulbs switched independently
13.	2	2	2	>X	bulbs switched independently
14.	2	2	2	1 bulb = X 1 bulb >X	bulbs switched independently

From the last experiment you should have discovered that cells may be connected in various ways. When the positive terminal of one cell is connected to the negative of another, the cells are said to be in *series*. When the positive terminals are connected together and the negative terminals are connected together, the cells are in *parallel*.

Fig. 264 represents different arrangements of two 1·5 volt dry cells. *What is the voltage across the terminals A and B in each of these diagrams?* (7) Use a voltmeter to check your answers.

Why are cells often wired in series? (8) *Is there any advantage to be gained by connecting them in parallel?* (9)

Draw the electrical circuit of a 3 volt torch. (10)

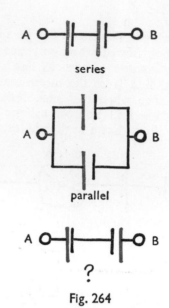

series

parallel

?

Fig. 264

The diagram in Fig. 265 shows part of a circuit often used to control one bulb from two switches each having three connections. You may have such an arrangement in your hall or staircase at home. *Can you complete this circuit and explain how it operates?* (11)

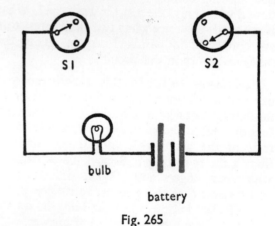

S1   S2

bulb

battery

Fig. 265

State what readings you would expect in each of the meters in Fig. 266 when

(a) *switch 1 is closed* (12)

(b) *switches 1 and 2 are closed and ammeter C reads 3 amps* (13)

(c) *all the switches are closed. Ammeter B reads 6 amps and ammeter C reads 2 amps.* (14)

How would each of the meter readings change
(i) if the resistance of R1 were increased and
(ii) the value of R3 were reduced? (15)

reason for this? What might happen if fuses
were not fitted in the mains circuits in your
home?

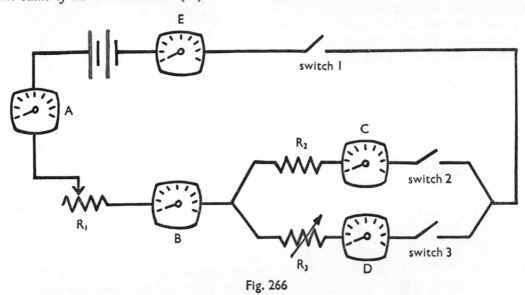

Fig. 266

Experiment 10.7. Connect up the circuit
shown in Fig. 267, making sure that the
positive terminal of the ammeter is wired to the
positive terminal of the accumulator. Set the

Draw a diagram showing what changes you
would make in the circuit shown in Fig. 267
to find the fusing current of a $\frac{1}{4}$ amp cartridge
fuse. At what current does it blow?

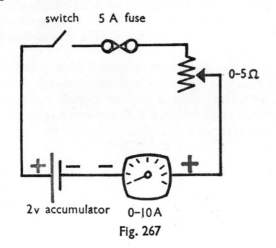

Fig. 267

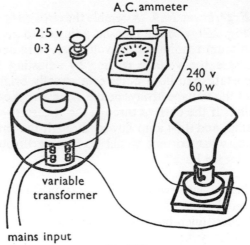

Fig. 268

rheostat so that all the resistance is in the
circuit. Close the switch and gradually increase
the current in the circuit by adjusting the rheostat. Why does the fuse 'blow' when the current
reaches a certain value? Did the wire melt
when 5 amp was flowing? Can you discover a

Watts are what matter

Demonstration 10.8. Using the circuit shown
in Fig. 268, gradually increase the input by
adjusting the variable transformer. What

happens to the brightness of each bulb as the voltage is increased? Does the current increase? Is the current the same in each bulb? Are they equally bright at any time? If the voltage were 240 volt and the potential difference across the torch bulb were 2·5 volt, what would be the voltage across the mains bulb?

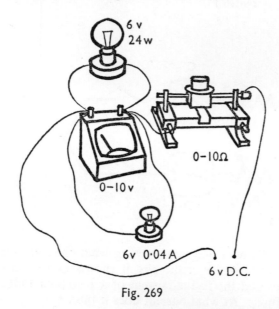

Fig. 269

Experiment 10.9. Assemble the circuit shown in Fig. 269 with the rheostat adjusted to give a minimum reading in the voltmeter. Gradually increase the voltage reading by adjusting the rheostat. Are both bulbs ever equally bright? Will the voltage always be the same across each bulb? If the current through the rheostat were 4 amp, and 0·04 amp flowed through the small bulb, what current would be flowing through the larger bulb?

In the last two experiments you have discovered that the amount of light energy produced by a bulb depends on the *current* and on the *voltage*. If either is increased, the energy used is increased. The amount of energy used every second (that is the rate of using energy) is called the *power*, and is found by multiplying the current (in amperes) by the potential difference (in volts). The power is then given in *joules per second* or *watts*.

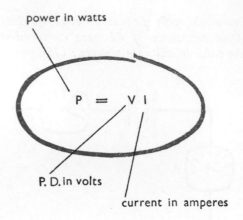

Most electrical appliances are rated in watts. This rating tells us the rate at which energy is *consumed by* the equipment, not the rate at which one type of energy is given out. A 40 watt fluorescent tube gives out far more light than a 40 watt tungsten filament bulb, yet they both *consume* the same amount of electrical energy every second. *What do you think has happened to the energy which has not been changed into light energy in the tungsten lamp?* (*16*) Modern discoveries and developments enable manufacturers to produce electric lamps which give more light for every watt they consume. *Could future discoveries enable electric heaters to give more heat than present ones for every watt they consume?* (*17*) *Explain your answer.* (*18*)

Find out the power consumed by a selection of electrical equipment such as an electric bulb, a smoothing iron, a one-bar electric radiator, an immersion heater, a T.V. receiver, a refrigerator, and a door bell. (*19*) *What is the power rating of a torch bulb?* (*20*)

Buying electrical energy

When you pay an electricity account you are paying for the number of joules you have used. A joule is the amount of energy supplied when 1 watt is taken for 1 second. As this is a very small quantity of energy, electricity is sold in units which represents the energy used in an hour at a rate of 1,000 watts. This is the Board of Trade 'unit' of electrical energy—the kilowatt hour (kWh). *How many joules are there in 1 kWh?* (*21*)

If a 'unit' of electricity costs 2d. how much will it cost to supply a 100 watt bulb for 100 hours? (22) What would be the cost of running a 3 kW immersion heater for the same time? (23) Assuming the mains voltage is 250 volt what would be the current in each case? (24)

If a 2·5 V 0·3 A torch bulb could be fully lit for 1 hour from a battery costing 6d. what is the cost of 1 kilowatt hour of such energy? (25) For how long could the same bulb be lit for 6d. by electricity costing 2d. per 'unit'? (26)

If you had to fit a fuse rated at 1 amp, 2 amp, 5 amp or 13 amp to electrical equipment rated as follows, which fuse would you choose for each? 60 watt, 100 watt, 300 watt, 600 watt, 1 kW, $1\frac{1}{2}$ kW, $2\frac{1}{2}$ kW. (27) In each case state the current you would expect to flow if the voltage were 250 volts. (28)

Visual aids

16 mm Sound Films

20.3841 Elements of Electrical Circuits$_{44}$

20.3845 Series and Parallel Circuits$_{44}$

Cells

This chapter is mainly descriptive and is not essential for the basic physics course. As much of the work described here will be done in the chemistry course, it need not be repeated. It has been included here for completeness.

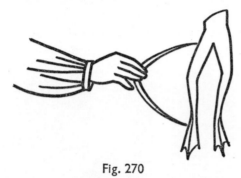

Fig. 270

Primary cells

'Animal Electricity'

'Lucia was skinning a few frogs to make soup'. So runs one legend associated with the wife of Professor Galvani of Bologna. When each frog was skinned she placed it on a metal dish lying near her husband's electrical machine. As she sat 'keeping her eyes on the delicate morsels', some students started to produce sparks from the machine. Suddenly Lucia saw the frogs' legs twitch as if they were alive. When Galvani repeated the experiment he also found this strange twitching whenever sparks were produced. He decided to see if lightning would produce similar results, and so, using brass hooks, he suspended some frogs on the iron railings surrounding the balcony of his house. One fine day when the sky was clear and a gentle wind was blowing, the legs twitched whenever they were blown against the railings. There was no lightning! This led him to try more experiments indoors. He placed the frogs' legs, with the brass hook attached, on an iron plate and pressed the hook against the plate. Each time 'he beheld the same twitchings'. Galvani explained this by saying that it was caused by 'indwelling animal electricity'.

Volta, another Italian, later showed that this mysterious twitching was due to the action of the two different metals and the fluid in the frogs' legs. Volta used two metals separated by a disc of flannel soaked in acetic acid, and thus constructed the first electric cell. By piling many of these cells one on top of the other he made a battery capable of developing a large electrical potential, which could cause a current to flow. This battery was called after its inventor the *Voltaic pile*. Volta's work aroused great interest and Napoleon invited him to Paris in 1801.

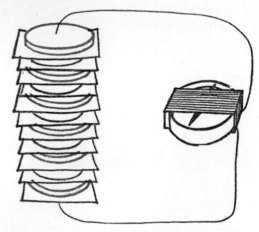

Fig. 271

Ammeters and Voltmeters

Experiment 11.1. You can build a simple Voltaic pile at home, using half a dozen pennies and large iron washers alternately. Thoroughly clean the discs with steel wool, and then separate each of them by a piece of blotting paper soaked in salt solution. To see if your battery will deliver current wind a coil of about 100 turns of very fine insulated wire on a cardboard former fixed round a compass. Connect the ends of the wire to the Voltaic pile as shown in Fig. 271. You have just constructed a simple kind of current-measuring device called a galvanometer. After whom do you think this instrument is named?

Demonstration 11.2. Wire the terminals of a 5,000 volt power unit to an electroscope. If the unit is not fitted with an internal voltmeter, connect one across the electroscope as shown in Fig. 272.

H.T. power unit

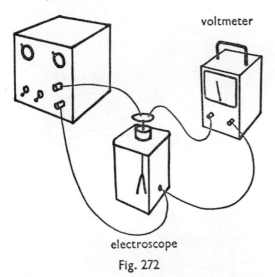

voltmeter

electroscope

Fig. 272

Gradually increase the output of the supply, watching the voltmeter needle and the electroscope leaves. Could an electroscope be used as a voltmeter? What do you think might be some of its disadvantages?

You can build a giant electroscope, using 2 ft lengths of $\frac{1}{2}$ in. aluminium tape connected to one terminal of the h.t. power unit. The other terminal should be earthed.

Warning. Make sure that the power unit is safe before you use it. It should be fitted with a very high resistance (for example, 20 MΩ) to prevent its supplying a dangerously large current.

In the above experiments two different types of instrument were used. In the first a galvanometer was used to indicate current. We normally refer to current measuring instruments as *ammeters*.

The second instrument, the electroscope, was used to indicate potential difference. Instruments designed for this purpose are called *voltmeters*. The electroscope passes no current once it is charged. It is not very robust, however, and is capable of measuring only very large voltages. In practice, therefore, we will be using instruments (moving coil instruments they are called) which do, unfortunately, pass a little current. By placing a high resistance in series with them they can be used as robust, reliable *voltmeters* for most purposes.

Electro-motive Force

The potential difference across a source of electrical energy which is driving no current through a circuit is called the electro-motive force (e.m.f.) of the source and is measured in volts. For this reason both the p.d. across part of a circuit and the e.m.f. of a source are sometimes referred to as 'voltages'. Ideally, the following experiment should be conducted using a voltmeter which passes no current. An electroscope is not suitable for such small voltages, but a Scalamp galvanometer (7891/S) used in series with a 1 Megohm resistor will give good results. The common type of meter suggested below will, however, be good enough to enable you to compare the e.m.fs developed across various pairs of metals.

Experiment 11.3. Connect a block of carbon to a high resistance voltmeter. A 0–1 mA meter in series with a 1,000 ohm resistor forms a suitable voltmeter (Fig. 273). Place a piece of filter paper soaked in copper sulphate solution or tap water on top of the carbon block, and press a clean copper (Cu) plate on top of the paper so that (say) two square inches of copper touch it. The copper plate should be connected to the negative terminal of the meter. Note the deflection of the needle.

Repeat this experiment, using the following metals, instead of the copper plate: lead (Pb), tin (Sn), iron (Fe), zinc (Zn), aluminium (Al) and magnesium (Mg). The metals should be thoroughly cleaned with emery paper before using them. Note the deflection obtained with each metal.

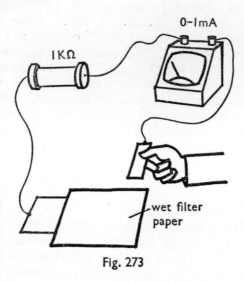

Fig. 273

As this meter takes a relatively large current, the area of contact alters the deflection. The same area, say two square inches, of each metal should therefore be placed in contact with the wet paper. A few inches of ribbon will suffice for magnesium. With meters passing practically no current the area of contact does not matter.

The results obtained from the last experiment are intended to indicate which metals produce large e.m.fs. Lead and aluminium produce misleading results because of other chemical actions which cannot easily be avoided with this simple apparatus. These metals will not therefore appear in their correct position in the electro-chemical series which you study in chemistry. Nevertheless, you should be able to discover which metals you might use to produce a large e.m.f.

Which two materials would make suitable positive plates for a cell? (1) Which two metals might be suitable for negative plates? (2) In practice magnesium, which is expensive, is not used.

Experiment 11.4. Push a copper plate and a zinc plate into a lemon. They should be about an inch apart. Use a 0–1 mA meter to detect the current.

E.m.f. and current

The e.m.f. produced between two metals in contact with an electrolyte depends only on the metals. The following experiments show how the *current* which flows as a result of this e.m.f. depends on various factors. Can you discover some of the things which affect the current?

Experiment 11.5.

(a) Pour about 100 cm³ of saturated sodium chloride (salt) solution into a small beaker, and place clean copper and zinc plates in the solution. Connect the plates to a voltmeter (for example a high resistance 0–3 V meter) and

Fig. 274

a bulb holder as shown in Fig. 274. Note the reading before and after screwing into the holder a small bulb (for example 2·5 V 0·2 A).

(b) Repeat this experiment, using 100 cm³ of dilute sulphuric acid (H_2SO_4). This is a *simple cell.*

Now add about 20 cm³ of a concentrated solution of potassium dichromate. What difference do you observe?

What is the effect of (1) bringing the plates closer together and (2) reducing the area of the plates immersed in the electrolyte?

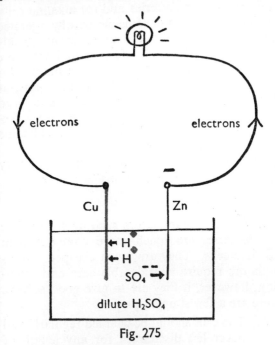

Fig. 275

The simple cell simplified!

When a simple cell is supplying a current, the zinc dissolves freely and the zinc plate becomes the negative pole. Zinc ions (Zn^{++}) must therefore be going into solution so that electrons are given up *to* the *external* circuit.

$$Zn \rightarrow Zn^{++} + 2e^-$$

The hydrogen ions from the dilute acid take electrons *from* the *external* circuit at the copper plate. Bubbles of hydrogen are therefore produced at the copper plate.

$$2H^+ + 2e^- \rightarrow 2H = H_2$$

Troubles in simple cells

The hydrogen bubbles which were formed at the positive (copper) plate of the simple cell are responsible for producing yet another cell action. This action produces an e.m.f. in opposition to the normal e.m.f. of the cell. It is called a *back e.m.f.* and the cell is said to be *polarised*. The addition of potassium dichromate quickly removes the hydrogen, as it

combines with the oxygen in potassium dichromate to form water. Such a substance is called a *depolarising agent*.

Commercial cells today use a variety of different metals for their electrodes and various solutions for their electrolytes and depolarising agents. The first cell of importance was invented by Professor Daniell of London in 1836. Later George Leclanché invented the forerunner of the *dry cell* (Fig. 276). Today mercury cells and manganese cells are rapidly gaining popularity as portable sources of electrical energy.

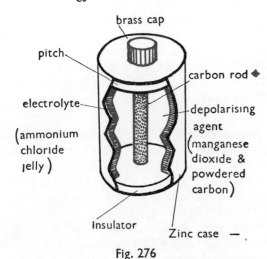

Fig. 276

Experiment 11.6. Study a selection of cells such as Daniell, Leclanché, dry, mercury and manganese cells. Measure and note the e.m.f. produced by each cell. Measure the e.m.f. of a very small and a very large dry cell. Why do you think manufacturers make large cells?

Fuel Cells

Over 100 years ago Sir William Grove demonstrated a 'gas battery' using hydrogen and oxygen. It is only within recent years, however, that this type of fuel cell has been developed commercially. A fuel cell is really a primary cell which uses cheap, normally gaseous, fuels, such as hydrogen and oxygen. The fuels are continuously fed into the cell as it operates. Such cells have already been used to power trucks and tractors, and it is thought that improved fuel cells will be essential for any attempt to land a man on the moon.

A biological fuel cell has also been produced which draws power from harmless bacteria. The bacteria are mixed with water and rice husks, which decompose as the bacteria feed on them. Such a cell can supply electricity to keep a radio receiver operating continuously for many years.

Secondary cells

All the cells which have been mentioned so far are called *primary cells*. Such cells will produce an e.m.f. and hence a current as soon as they are constructed. After having been in use for some time, however, primary cells, other than fuel cells, are exhausted and must be scrapped. They cannot normally be recharged satisfactorily.

Demonstration 11.7. Construct a simple lead-acid cell by placing two clean lead plates in a solution of dilute sulphuric acid (for example density = $1 \cdot 2$ g/cm³). Connect a torch bulb (for example $2 \cdot 5$ V $0 \cdot 3$ A) across the cell and see if it lights up.

Now pass a direct current of 2 amperes through the cell for two minutes, switch off the current, and again connect the bulb across the cell. What do you conclude from this experiment?

Secondary cells are cells which can be revived! They are really used to store electrical energy in a chemical form. The simplest secondary cell may be made as in the above experiment by placing two lead plates in dilute sulphuric acid and passing a direct current through the cell for several hours. The cell is said to be *charged* and is then capable of producing a current in the *opposite* direction to the direction of the charging current.

Secondary cells are of two main types (*a*) lead acid accumulators, which have been developed from the cell described above and are used in car batteries and (*b*) alkaline cells, such as those used in some electrically operated vehicles. Alkaline cells can be more quickly charged than the lead acid type and are more robust. They are particularly suitable for emergency supplies in hospitals and trains, as they do not deteriorate so rapidly as do lead acid accumulators when not in use. Rechargeable flashlights also operate from alkaline (nickel-cadmium) cells.

In general, secondary cells can supply very much larger currents than primary cells.

Care of Accumulators

Lead acid accumulators such as are used in car batteries are much more common than alkaline cells. They are much cheaper. Accumulators require considerable care and attention, however, if they are to give good service. Here are a few simple tips.

(*a*) The cells should be charged regularly and never left discharged for any length of time.

(*b*) The acid level should be maintained by adding distilled water regularly.

(*c*) The terminals should be kept clean and smeared with grease.

(*d*) The cells should not be subjected to rough handling!

(*e*) The cells should not be short-circuited, that is, they should not be allowed to drive very large currents (for example 100 amp).

(*f*) The charging rate stated on the cell should not be exceeded.

To find if the accumulator is charged or discharged the density of the electrolyte is measured. The instrument used for this purpose is called a hydrometer.

Visual aids

Charts

Nife Cell₄₅
Mercury-Zinc Alkaline Dry Cells₃₇

16 mm Sound Films

20.3844 Primary Cell₄₄

Magnetic Magic

CHAPTER 12

Charges in motion

You have already met three types of action-at-a-distance forces: gravity, electric force and magnetism. The basis of magnetism, described by André Ampère, is illustrated by the following experiment. It shows how magnetism and electricity are related.

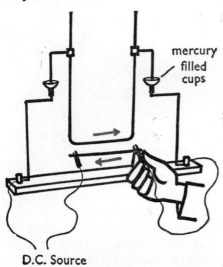

Fig. 277

Demonstration 12.1.

(*a*) With the apparatus₂ illustrated in Fig. 277 we can study the effects of an electric current flowing in the same or opposite directions in two parallel conductors. A copper wire is pivoted just above its centre of gravity so that it is free to swing on two points resting in mercury filled cups.

What is the effect of bringing a second copper wire parallel to it as shown (i) when a current of at least 10 amp flows in the same direction in both wires and (ii) when the current flows in opposite directions? What is the effect of bringing the two conductors closer together? How does the force between the conductors alter as the current is reduced?

(*b*) A simpler alternative experiment may be conducted with two-foot lengths of ½ in.

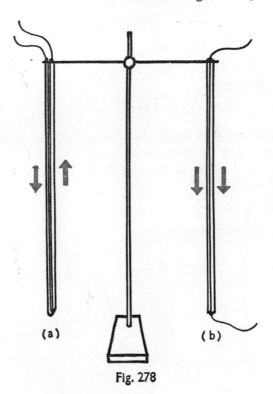

Fig. 278

aluminium tape₄ connected as shown in Fig. 278. In the first case the currents are in opposite directions, and in the second they are in the same direction. The tapes should be about ¼ in. apart and a current of 10–15 amp passed through them. State how the forces act in each case.

Demonstration 12.2. Connect a cathode ray tube to an induction coil, and find the direction in which the electrons are moving. Now place a heavy copper wire above the tube, or attach aluminium tape to the tube with Sellotape. Allow a current of several amperes to flow so

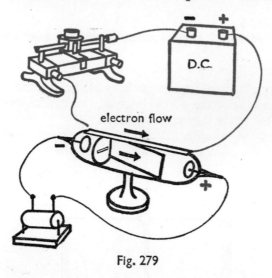

Fig. 279

that the electrons in the wire move in the same direction as those in the tube. What is the result? Reverse the current in the wire and note the result.

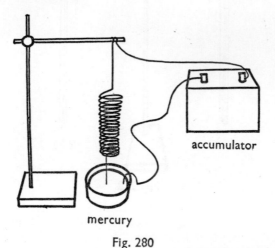

Fig. 280

Demonstration 12.3. Suspend a close-wound 1 in diameter coil of thin insulated wire so that one end dips into a pool of mercury, and connect up the circuit as shown in Fig. 280. What kind of force do you think acts between adjacent turns? Is the current flowing in the same direction in adjacent turns?

Demonstration 12.4. Suspend two coils of wire by strips of aluminium tape as shown in Fig. 281. Coils having a 3 in diameter and

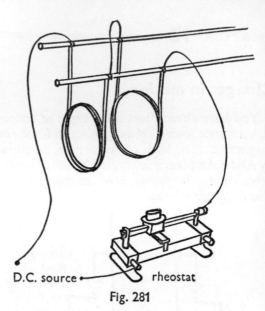

Fig. 281

about 30 turns are suitable. Connect them up so that a current of about 6 amp flows in the same direction through the coils. What happens when they are brought fairly close together? Reverse the current in *one coil*. How does this affect their behaviour?

From these experiments it is clear that a mechanical force is exerted on electrons in motion (electric current) when another electric current is flowing nearby. If the electrons are moving in a wire a force is exerted on the wire; if they are moving in space the electron beam itself is bent. This mutual force between electric charges in motion we call *magnetism*. The force increases as the currents increase, and disappears completely if one current is switched off. The force increases as the conductors are brought closer together, and is reversed if one current is reversed. Finally, the most important 'rule' we have discovered is that

currents in the same direction attract each other
currents in opposite directions repel each other

We will use this discovery to construct a simple electric motor.

The electric motor

Demonstration 12.5. Wind a rectangular coil of six turns of 22 s.w.g. insulated wire. Place this coil round a Russian earth motor[18] as shown in Fig. 282. The motor coil should be

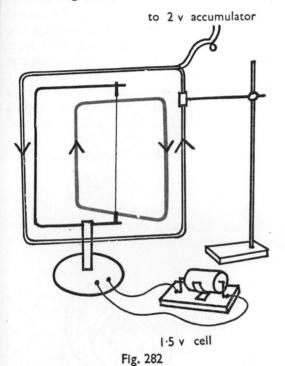

to 2 v accumulator

1·5 v cell

Fig. 282

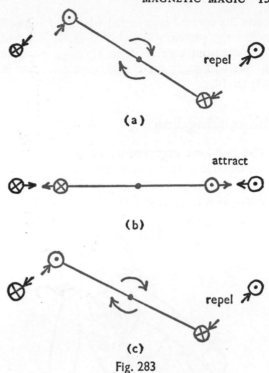

(a)

repel

attract

(b)

(c)

Fig. 283

free to rotate inside the fixed coil. Sides of the coils in which current is flowing in the same direction will attract each other, and those in which current is flowing in opposite directions will repel each other.

Fig. 283 shows a plan view of cross sections of the coils. The dot represents the point of a dart and indicates that electrons are coming out of the paper. The cross represents the tail feathers of the dart and indicates that the electrons are going into the paper.

If the coils are in the position shown in Fig. 283(*a*), the motor coil will rotate to position (*b*). If at that instant the current flowing through the motor coil is reversed, the coil will continue to rotate through position (*c*). If the current is switched at the right time the motor will rotate continuously.

This reversing may be done automatically by fixing a device called a *commutator* to the rotating coil as shown in Fig. 284. By this

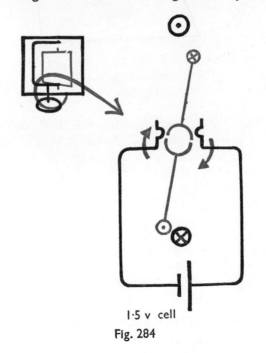

1·5 v cell

Fig. 284

means the current is reversed whenever the coil reaches the position shown in Fig. 283(*b*) and its momentum carries it on through position (*c*). We will study the electric motor further in Chapter 14.

The missing link

The previous experiments have shown that when electric currents flow they exert a force on one another. Is this really the same kind of force as a magnet exerts on iron filings?

Fig. 285

Experiment 12.6. Bare the ends and centre of a metre length of 22 s.w.g. copper wire. Connect *one* end to a large-capacity 2 volt accumulator and hold the middle in some fine iron filings (Fig. 285). Will the bare copper wire pick up the filings?

Now complete the circuit by touching the free end of the wire on the accumulator terminal *for a second or so.* Does the wire attract the filings while the current is flowing? What happens when the current stops?

Until about 150 years ago, no one had discovered any connection between electricity and the mysterious forces which cause lodestone to attract certain metals and a compass needle to point in a north-south direction.

For about fourteen years Professor Oersted of Copenhagen had searched, without success, for such a connection. Then one day in 1819 he was lecturing on the simple cell. At the end of his lecture he used the cell to drive a current through a length of wire which was lying *parallel* to a compass needle. To his surprise and that of his students the needle immediately moved! On previous occasions he had always placed the wire at right angles to the compass needle. Moral—'If at first you don't succeed . . .'

You can repeat Oersted's experiment quite simply as follows.

Experiment 12.7.

(*a*) Allow a compass needle to settle in a north-south direction. Using the apparatus shown in Fig. 286, with the switch open hold a

Fig. 286

length of wire above and parallel to the compass needle. Ask someone to switch on the current for a few seconds. What happens to the compass needle? Note the direction in which it moves and the direction in which the electrons are moving in the circuit.

(b) Repeat this experiment with the wire placed below the compass needle. What happens?

(c) Repeat (a) and (b) with the accumulator reversed and record the results obtained.

10 watt 0·5 ohm resistors[13] are suitable for this and the next experiment.

Now switch on the current and again note how they point. Repeat this experiment with the compasses in different positions on the board. How do the needles point when a current flows through the wire? Reverse the current and describe what happens.

It is sometimes useful to refer to the direction in which the *north pole* of a small compass points. In fact we often draw lines which indicate this direction. These magnetic field lines are sometimes referred to as *lines of force*. Remember that they simply indicate the direction in which the compass needle points. In the case of a straight wire such as that used

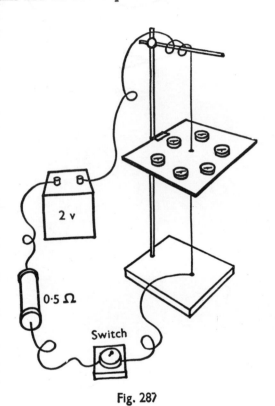

Fig. 287

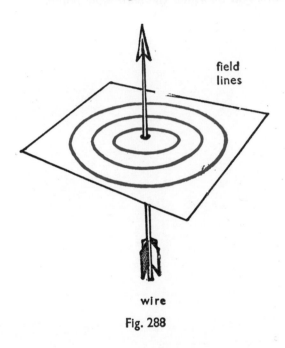

field lines

wire

Fig. 288

Experiment 12.8. Fix a hardboard square to a burette stand using terry clips, and stretch a length of wire through a hole in the square as shown in Fig. 287. Connect the wire to a 2 volt accumulator via a switch and a ½ ohm resistor. Place half a dozen plotting compasses[2] on the hardboard and note the direction in which they point.

in Experiment 12.8 the field lines can be represented as circles round the wire (Fig. 288).

For many purposes it is enough to know that the field lines are as shown in Fig. 288. Sometimes, however, it is necessary to know whether compass needles point clockwise or anti-clockwise round a wire. Some books give a number of rules based on conventional (positive charge) current. As we have been considering electric current through wires as the movement of electrons we will continue to use the electron direction in stating our (anti-corkscrew!!) rule (Fig. 289).

All the information about fields that you are likely to need at this stage can be obtained from the simple rule.

When the electrons are coming towards you (out of the paper) the direction of the field is clockwise.

Test this rule by using the apparatus of Experiment 12.8. *Describe how the results of Oersted's experiment confirm this rule?* (*1*) Remember that the direction of the field is the direction in which the *north pole* points.

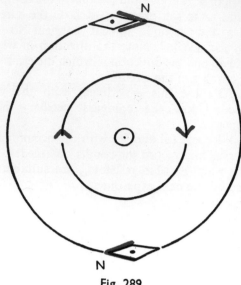

Fig. 289

Canned currents

CHAPTER 13

Permanent Magnets

In the following experiments we will investigate the behaviour of permanent magnets. Remembering that when electric charges move a magnetic field is produced, we will then try to construct a model to explain the properties of permanent magnets.

Fig. 290

Experiment 13.1. For this experiment you will require an unmagnetised knitting needle. Use a compass to test that it is not a magnet. To do this you must make sure that *both* ends of the knitting needle *attract* the same pole of the compass.

Now magnetise the needle using, say, the *north pole* of an Alnico magnet (Fig. 290). If you draw the magnet's *north pole* towards X does X become a *north* or a *south* pole when the needle is magnetised? Test your answer with a compass needle. Remember that you can be sure that the needle is a magnet only if it *repels* one end of the compass.

Experiment 13.2. Using the needle magnetised in Experiment 13.1, cut it through the middle and test the ends of each piece with a compass. What did you find? Halve one of the halves and test it. Can you separate the north and south poles of a magnet in this way?

The last experiment has shown that you cannot separate the north and south poles of a magnet by cutting it. *Is the same true of an electrically charged body with positive charges at one end and negative charges at the other? (1) Describe an experiment you might use to justify your answer. (2)*

Suppose it were possible to go on splitting up the knitting needle into smaller and smaller pieces, would each piece still have two poles? The following experiment may point to an answer.

Fig. 291

Experiment 13.3. Fill a small test tube with iron filings and bring one end of the tube towards the *north* and then the *south pole* of a stationary compass needle. Does the test tube behave like a bar magnet or like an unmagnetised magnetic material such as iron? Now draw the *north pole* of an Alnico magnet several times along the test tube in one direction (Fig. 291). Repeat the above test and state the result obtained. Finally, shake the test tube and repeat the test. What do you discover?

It would seem that each iron filing is capable of behaving like a little magnet. When the filings are magnetised by stroking in one direction they 'line up' to produce a strong *field. What happens to the magnetic field when the filings are shaken? (3) Why? (4)*

Are iron filings the smallest magnets that can exist, or might there be even smaller 'atomic magnets'? The following experiment helps us to investigate this guess (hypothesis).

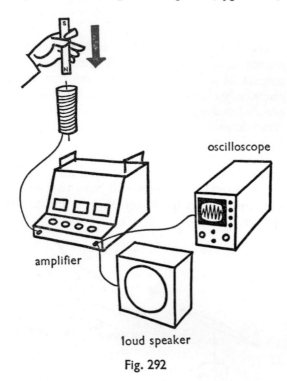

oscilloscope

amplifier

loud speaker

Fig. 292

Demonstration 13.4. Barkhausen effect. In this experiment a 400-turn coil of wire$_{2,4}$ is connected to the input of a sensitive audio amplifier$_7$. The coil should be connected to the low impedance input socket, and the output fed to a loudspeaker and, if possible, an oscilloscope. The amplifiers of certain tape recorders are suitable for this experiment, provided they have low impedance microphone sockets.

Fix a steel rod in the solenoid. A bicycle spoke has been found to give satisfactory results. With the amplifier switched on bring the north pole of a magnet slowly towards the end of the steel rod but don't let them touch. Repeat this operation several times. The hiss heard in the speaker is due to irregular magnetic fluctuations near, or in, the solenoid. Can you

think of a way of testing whether or not the steel rod is responsible for this hiss? Is it?

Repeat the original experiment   Does the hiss become greater or less with successive thrusts of the magnet? Why might this be?

Now remove the magnet, turn it round, and bring the south pole towards the steel rod. What do you hear?

The last experiment showed that a hiss was produced only when a steel bar was in the coil. Something must be happening in the steel when a magnet is brought close to it. The simplest explanation is that there are tiny 'atomic magnets' in the metal, some of which rotate when the magnet is brought near. Once they have come 'into line' with the field the hiss produced by further thrusts of the magnet is greatly reduced. This model of a permanent magnet is shown in Fig. 293.

unmagnetised

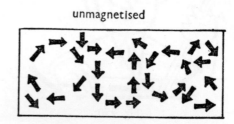

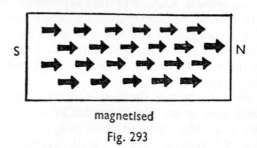

magnetised

Fig. 293

If the atomic magnets in a substance are higgledy-piggledy (like the iron filings after they have been shaken up), the magnetic effects of these magnets will tend to cancel each other and the substance will not behave as a magnet. In this state the atomic magnets may arrange themselves in a series of closed loops. If, however, the atomic magnets are 'lined up' so that they point in one direction, their effects will add up to produce a strong magnetic field. The substance will then behave as a magnet.

Using this model, which pole of the atomic magnets would you expect to rotate to face X in Fig. 290? (5) Does your answer agree with experimental results? (6)

Assuming that a steel rod has been magnetised so that the atomic magnets are in line, what do you think might happen to these atomic magnets if the rod were strongly heated? (7) The following experiment will enable you to test your prediction.

Experiment 13.5. Magnetise a knitting needle and test it with a compass. Now heat the needle *strongly* in a bunsen flame. Test it again. Has it lost its magnetism? What has happened to the atomic magnets?

Domain Theory

The 'atomic magnet' hypothesis is supported by the experiments you have conducted. Such a model is quite adequate for all the work you will be doing in this course. The somewhat fuller discussion given below cannot be illustrated by simple school experiments. Nevertheless it is probably worth taking on trust for the time being.

magnetic substance

(unmagnetised)

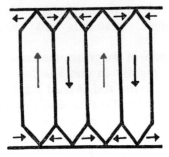

no external magnetic field

Fig. 294

We have seen that when electric charges move, a magnetic field is produced. Even permanent magnets owe their magnetism to the movement of electric charges (electrons) in their atoms, each electron producing its own tiny magnetic field. As the electrons rotate in their orbits, or spin on their axes, they produce the same kind of effect as an electric current in a coil. In magnetic materials such as iron these 'atomic magnets' form into large groups or *domains* which behave rather like minute iron filings, each domain being a magnet. It is now thought that the domains in an unmagnetised magnetic material may be arranged as shown in Fig. 294.

When the substance is placed in a magnetic field, some of the atomic magnets rotate so that

microscope pictures of a barium ferrite crystal

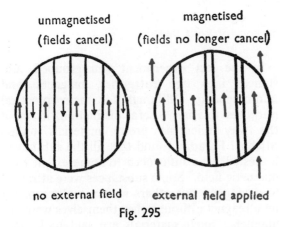

Fig. 295

the domains whose axes point in the direction of the magnetic field grow bigger at the expense of the others. These changes in the boundaries of the domains have actually been observed and photographed using a microscope (Fig. 295).

In some materials, such as soft iron, the domains return to their original arrangement when the field is removed, so that the material loses its magnetism. In other materials, such as steel, the domains retain their new pattern and the material retains its magnetism.

In addition to the changes in domain boundaries it is possible, under the influence of strong magnetic fields, for all the atoms in a domain to swing round so that the magnetic axes of these domains point in the direction of the field. The material is then said to be fully magnetised or *saturated*.

Magnetic materials

You have already discovered that some materials can be picked up by magnets and others cannot. In the following experiment you are asked to discover as many magnetic materials as possible. Some materials are very weakly magnetic and this test may put them in the 'non-magnetic' group.

Experiment 13.6. Use a long compass needle to identify materials$_{4,8}$ which can be attracted by, or attract, a magnet. List the materials under the headings 'magnetic materials' and 'non-magnetic materials'. Do you think that all substances which can be picked up by a magnet will attract a compass needle? Give a reason for your answer.

In the last experiment you grouped substances into two categories, magnetic and non-magnetic. Although for many practical purposes this is a useful distinction, it is not the way scientists group materials today. Michael Faraday found that all the substances he tested were influenced to some extent by a magnetic field. Some substances were attracted to a magnet, but others were actually repelled by a magnet although they themselves were not magnets. Such materials are said to be *diamagnetic*.

Experiment 13.7.

(*a*) Suspend a small rod of bismuth between the poles of a large electromagnet so that it lies in the position shown in Fig. 296. Make certain that no iron filings are attached to it. Now switch on the current and see what happens. In what way does its behaviour differ from that of a piece of iron? Is bismuth diamagnetic? Copper, gold, glass, water and mercury are also weakly repelled by a magnet.

If necessary, a small bismuth rod can be made by pouring molten bismuth into a suitably shaped cavity in moulding sand.

(*b*) If a large electromagnet is not available, suspend the bismuth rod by a thread and allow it to come to rest. Now bring the poles of a large permanent horse-shoe magnet towards the bismuth rod until they surround it in the position illustrated in Fig. 296. What happens to the bismuth?

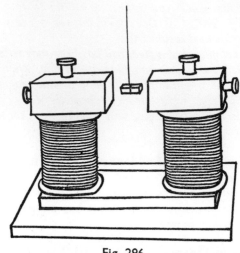

Fig. 296

The substances which are strongly attracted to a magnet are called *ferromagnetic* because they behave like iron (Latin: ferrum). They include iron, nickel and cobalt. Where do these elements come in the periodic table? Many alloys such as mu-metal are also ferromagnetic. The materials which are normally referred to as magnetic substances are ferromagnetic. Many other substances are so weakly attracted that under normal conditions a magnet seems to have no effect on them. They are called paramagnetic. Most of the 'non-magnetic' materials are really paramagnetic.

One group of magnetic materials has been developed rapidly in the last few years—the *ferrites*. A ferrite rod is used inside the aerial of a transistor radio thus enabling the size of the aerial to be reduced considerably. Ferrites are also used extensively in a computor's 'memory', a device for storing information magnetically. Ferrites have the interesting property of being strongly magnetic although they are electrical insulators. Fig. 295 shows the movement of domain boundaries in a piece of ferrite known under the trade name of Ferroxdure. This particular ferrite is used to make powerful permanent magnets.

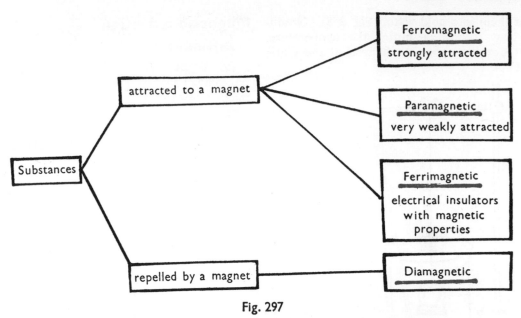

Fig. 297

Modern Magnets

Permanent magnets have undergone many dramatic developments during the twentieth century. In 1917 two Japanese physicists, Honda and Takei, added cobalt to tungsten steel to make powerful magnets. Another Japanese discovery in 1932 produced even stronger magnets from alloys of iron, nickel and aluminium. Since then many new alloys have appeared under such trade names as Alcomax, Alnico, Hycomax and Iconal.

Today powerful permanent magnets are being made from these alloys and from ceramic materials. The poles may be near the ends or the faces of the magnets. A wide range of such magnets used in the electronics industry is now available[9]. Magnetic rubber strip is often used on refrigerator doors. Rolls of this strip are readily available in tool shops.

You should examine some of these magnets and investigate their fields. *Can you discover where permanent magnets are used in some of the following: transistor radios, ammeters and voltmeters, television sets, telephone hand sets, refrigerator and cupboard doors, maximum and minimum thermometers? (8). Can you find any other uses for permanent magnets? (9)*

Audio and video recorders use magnetic tapes of such a quality that the recorded programmes are practically indistinguishable from the originals. The tape used is coated with particles of a magnetic oxide of iron, which are in the form of tiny needles so small that each is a single magnetic domain. As each domain is separate from its neighbour the domains can be magnetised in different directions without interfering with each other. Intense research is continually developing better magnetic materials, which are used in tape recorders to produce good quality reproduction at lower tape speeds.

Temperature

When a magnetised knitting needle was strongly heated it lost its magnetism. If it had been heated to an even higher temperature, it would have ceased to be ferromagnetic. The temperature at which this happens is called the Curie point. In the following experiment you can find the Curie point of an alloy.

Experiment 13.8. Jae metal contains 70 per cent nickel and 30 per cent copper. Attach a piece of this metal[4,10] to a small magnet and lower them into cold water (Fig. 298). Gradually heat the water noting the temperature. What do you expect to happen at the Curie point?

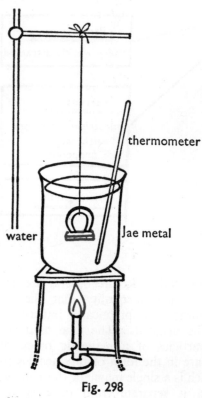

Fig. 298

Experiment 13.9. Attach a few tacks to a magnet as shown in Fig. 299. Strongly heat one of the tacks with a bunsen burner and explain the result.

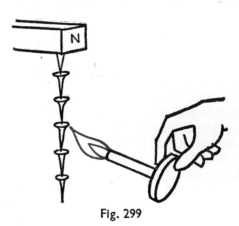

Fig. 299

Magnetic induction

Experiment 13.10.

(*a*) Attach a long nail to the *south pole* of a bar magnet as shown in Fig. 300. Bring another magnet towards the lower end of the nail and determine by repulsion whether Y is a *north* or a *south pole*. Why will only a test of repulsion determine this? What is the polarity of X? X and Y are called *induced poles*.

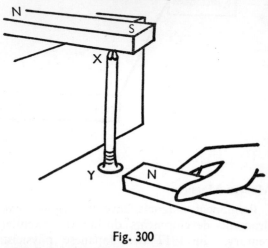

Fig. 300

(*b*) Explain what happens when two 3 in nails are suspended, side by side, on the end of a magnet.

Experiment 13.11. Suspend a 'chain' of tacks from the end of a bar magnet. What happens when you separate the magnet from the top tack? Why is this?

When a magnet is brought close to a magnetic material such as iron (Fig. 301), some of the

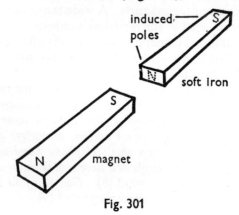

Fig. 301

domains change so that the material becomes a magnet. This process is called *magnetic induction*. When the magnet is removed, most of the domains return to their original state so that the iron is no longer a magnet. Materials which behave like this are said to be *non-retentive* or magnetically *soft*. Magnetically soft materials, such as iron, mumetal and Permalloy C are used in the cores of electro-magnets and transformers. They lose their magnetism as soon as the current is switched off.

In other materials such as steel many of the domains 'stay put', so that the steel retains its magnetism. The steel is said to be *retentive* or magnetically *hard*. Special materials such as Alnico are often used in preference to steel for permanent magnets. These materials are very retentive.

Can you explain in terms of induced poles (a) why a magnet picks up iron nails and (b) what happens to a compass needle if a soft iron block is brought close to it? (10)

Magnetic fields

If a plotting compass is placed near a magnet it always comes to rest pointing in a definite direction. Suppose the compass is placed near the south pole of a magnet (position A, Fig. 302)

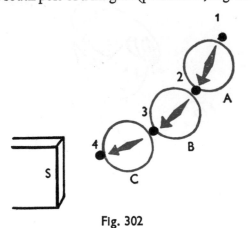

Fig. 302

it will point in the direction shown. If now the head and tail (that is the *north* and *south* ends) of the compass needle are marked on a piece of paper (marks 1 and 2), the compass can be

moved so that its tail now points to mark 2 (position B), and a new mark (3) can be made to indicate the position of the head of the compass. This procedure can be repeated (position C) and a further mark (4) made on the paper. If now the points (1, 2, 3 and 4) are joined up, a line is produced which indicates the direction in which the *north pole* of the compass needle always points. *What is such a line called? (11)* Although in this experiment it is possible to produce lines in only two dimensions (the plane of the paper) remember that the magnetic field exists in the space (three dimensions) all round the magnet.

Fascinating three dimensional field patterns can be produced by using very fine nickel powder[10] instead of iron filings.

Magnetic field lines are sometimes defined as 'the direction in which a "free" *north pole* would move'. As we cannot obtain a free *north pole*, that is one which is quite separate from a *south pole*, this definition is not very helpful. We can, however, use a long magnet so that the *south pole* is some distance from the *north pole*. Under such conditions the *north pole* behaves, to some extent, as if it were 'free'.

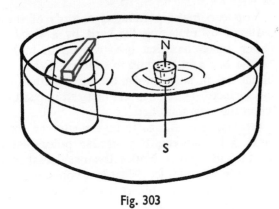

Fig. 303

Experiment 13.12. Magnetise a needle and push it through a cork so that it will float with its *north pole* above water. Place a bar magnet on an inverted tumbler so that it lies just above the water surface (Fig. 303). Investigate the movement of the 'free' *north pole* when it is released close to various parts of the bar magnet.

Experiment 13.13.

(*a*) Use plotting compasses to produce field patterns of (i) a bar magnet (ii) two bar magnets with their opposite poles about 3 in apart and (iii) two bar magnets lying with their *south poles* about 3 in apart (Fig. 304).

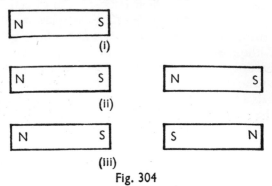

Fig. 304

(*b*) Repeat the above experiments using iron filings to produce the field patterns. A card or sheet of glass should be placed on the magnets and a pepper pot used to sprinkle a thin layer of filings on to it. Are the patterns produced by the compasses and the iron filings similar? What additional information do the compasses provide?

You can make permanent records of these patterns by replacing the card by a sheet of paper which has first been dipped in molten candle wax and hung up to solidify. When the filings are in position run a bunsen flame over the surface. The filings will be fixed in position when the wax solidifies.

(*c*) Use iron filings to investigate the magnetic field between two similar poles placed about 3 in apart. Notice the cushion-shaped region in the middle. What can you say about the iron filings at the centre of this region? What does this suggest? This point is called the *neutral point*.

(*d*) Can you find any neutral points when a bar magnet is placed with its north pole (*a*) facing north and (*b*) facing south?

(*e*) Finally you may like to investigate the magnetic fields round the apparatus illustrated in Fig. 305. What can you say about the field inside the ring? This is an example of 'magnetic screening'.

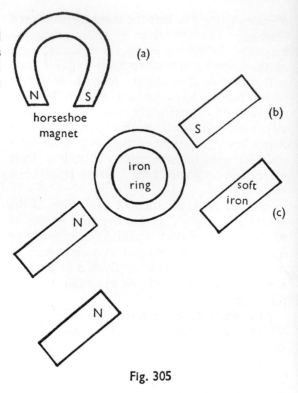

Fig. 305

Experiment 13.14. Take a 3 in Alnico magnet and, using a 50 gram spring balance or even a nail, find where along its length the

Fig. 306

magnet exerts the greatest pull. How is this region related to the field lines?

The Earth as a magnet

More than 2,000 years ago the Greeks were aware of the peculiar properties of two minerals, amber and lodestone. They knew that if a piece of amber was rubbed it would pick up certain light objects, and that lodestone attracted iron without being rubbed. Lodestone or magnetite is found in many parts of the world, including the Cuillin Hills. It has been suggested that the Chinese may have discovered that a piece of lodestone freely suspended always came to rest pointing in the same direction. The Chinese Emperor, Hwang-Ti, is said to have used a primitive compass on his chariot about 250 B.C.

Fig. 307

We have no definite evidence, however, that this property was known before the early Middle Ages. In 1269 Petrus Peregrinus, a French Crusader, gave the first detailed descriptions of a floating compass and a pocket compass similar to those we use today.

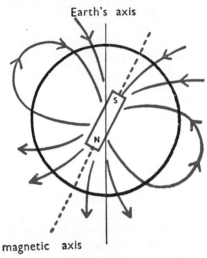

Fig. 308

About 400 years ago William Gilbert of Colchester, Queen Elizabeth's physician, suggested that the Earth itself behaved as if it were a huge magnet. He built a model of the Earth made of lodestone, and discovered that it had a magnetic field around it similar to the Earth's field. The cause of the Earth's field is still not really understood, although various theories have been suggested. It seems likely that it is caused by electric charges moving within the Earth's liquid core (dynamo theory). 'What causes these charges to move?' you may ask. One guess is that heat is produced in the core by radio-activity. This heat then causes the molten core to swirl around rather like soup in a saucepan. Whatever may be the mechanism of the Earth's magnetism, the field produced is certainly similar to the field we might expect if the Earth contained a giant bar magnet!

Experiment 13.15.

(a) Construct a floating compass using a Ticonal E magnet (M2702), placed on a slice of cork.

(b) Alternatively, use an Eclipse Alnico magnet placed on two watch glasses, or floating on a large cork.

The end of the magnet which always points north was originally called the 'north-seeking pole'. In time this was abbreviated to the *north pole*. As a magnetic *north pole* is attracted to a magnetic *south pole* the Earth's geographic north pole must be magnetically *south*! This is, of course, a man-made paradox which results from *defining* the *north pole* of a compass as the end which points north.

Declination

The magnetic *north pole* and the geographic north pole do not coincide. This is of great importance to mariners using a magnetic compass to guide them. In the following experiment you can discover the angle between 'true north' (that is geographic north) and 'magnetic *north*' (as indicated by a compass) in your part of the world.

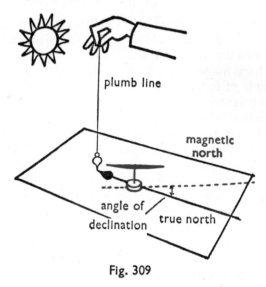

plumb line

magnetic north

angle of declination   true north

Fig. 309

Experiment 13.16. Fix a plumb line so that it casts a shadow on a piece of paper when the sun is at its highest point (noon). This shadow will lie in a north-south direction pointing to the geographic north pole. Now place a compass on the shadow, and draw a line indicating the direction in which it points. The

angle between these lines is called the angle of *declination*. Measure this angle.

In addition to discovering America, Columbus discovered that the compass does not everywhere point towards the Pole Star. During his voyage from Spain to the West Indies he found that the compass direction kept varying. This erratic behaviour of the compass caused panic amongst the crew, and only Columbus' powers of persuasion saved the day. He convinced the sailors that it was the Pole Star and not the compass which was misbehaving!

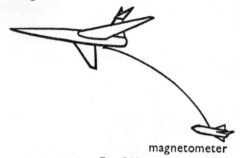

magnetometer

Fig. 310

A world survey has shown how the angle of declination changes from place to place. In making such surveys, instruments for measuring the strength of the Earth's magnetic field (magnetometers) are towed by aircraft (Fig. 310). To enable mariners to calculate the geographic north from the compass direction, charts have been constructed indicating the different angles of declination. They are called isogonic charts.

Dip

Model 13.17. Pull a trolley along a bench using a thread held at different angles to the horizontal (Fig. 311). If A, B and C represent three points one above the other you will see

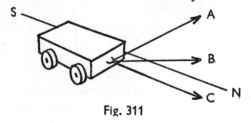

Fig. 311

that the trolley moves in a horizontal plane in the direction SN regardless of the angle the thread makes with the horizontal.

The compass needles we have so far used rotate only in a horizontal plane. They do not, therefore, tell us whether the Earth's field has a horizontal direction or whether the lines of force make an angle with the horizontal. Nearly 400 years ago Robert Norman, a London compass-maker, decided to suspend a compass needle at its centre of gravity so that it could rotate in a vertical plane as it lay in the north-south direction. He discovered that it dipped with its *north pole* downwards. *Would he have obtained the same results had he lived south of the magnetic equator?* (*12*)

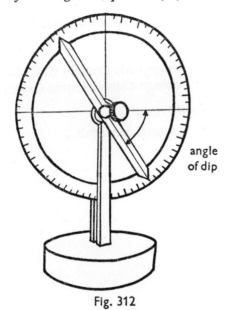

angle
of dip

Fig. 312

A compass needle mounted in this way is called a *dip circle* or *dipping needle*, and the angle between the horizontal and the direction of the needle is called the *angle of dip*.

Changes in declination and dip

It has been found that the imaginary magnet in the Earth does not lie still! Gradually, over hundreds of years, the angles of declination and dip have been changing. These variations, due to changes within the Earth, are called secular changes. In addition, daily variations of the

Earth's field have been observed. They are much smaller than the secular changes, and are thought to be caused by the movement of ionised layers surrounding the Earth. These layers are affected by the amount of ultra-violet radiation reaching them from the sun, and this in turn is affected by sunspot activity. In 1964 there was very little sunspot activity and it was known as the 'year of the quiet sun'.

Magnetic Induction Due to the Earth's Field

In the following experiments you can compare the magnetic induction in magnetically soft (non-retentive) and hard (retentive) substances.

We have seen from the dip circle that the vertical part of the Earth's magnetic field is strong in this country. This vertical *component*, as it is called, may be used to induce magnetism in both types of magnetic material.

Permalloy C

Fig. 313

Experiment 13.18. This is a fascinating experiment which you can use later to baffle your friends. Hold vertically a piece of Permalloy C or Mumetal. It is so 'soft' that the Earth's field turns it into a magnet. Hold the bottom of the metal strip close to a compass needle and note the result (Fig. 313). Was the bottom of the strip a *north* or a *south pole*? Now move the strip vertically downwards until its top edge is close to the compass. What is the polarity of the top edge? Turn the metal strip upside down and repeat this experiment. Can you explain the results?

Permalloy C and other materials for many excellent experiments in magnetism are available to schools from the International Nickel Company[10].

Experiment 13.19.

(a) Test a 4 in nail or steel bar with a compass to make sure that it is not a magnet.

Explain how you did this. Now hold the nail vertically and hammer it several times. What effect will this have on the domains? Again test the nail carefully with a compass. Is it now magnetised permanently?

(b) Use a compass needle to test railings, radiators and retort stands to see if they have been magnetised by the Earth's field.

Steel structures such as bridges, and in particular those subjected to vibration, often become magnetised by the Earth's field. *If a vertical girder were so magnetised what would be the polarity of its lower end?* (13)

Visual aids

Charts

Science for Today. No. 13. Electricity in the Sky and Magnetism in the Earth[36]

Filmstrips

E52 History of Magnetism[51]

8 mm Cassettes

80-203 Ferromagnetic Domain Wall Motion[40]
80-204 Paramagnetism of Liquid Oxygen[40]

16 mm Sound Films

Modern Magnetic Materials[39]

Electro-magnetism

CHAPTER 14

Solenoids

When an electric current flows through a conductor a magnetic field is produced round the wire. *Can you describe the field around a straight wire which is carrying current? (1)* You will be able to investigate the field around a coil of wire in the next experiment.

2 v accumulator

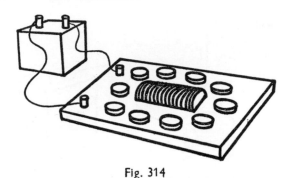

Fig. 314

Experiment 14.1. A coil of 30 turns of plastic covered 22 s.w.g. wire is wound on a piece of hardboard₁₁ as shown in Fig. 314. The coil is then connected to a 2 volt accumulator through a 0·5 ohm resistor.

Place a sheet of paper on the hardboard and use plotting compasses to plot the field around and within the solenoid. Does the field resemble any field you have already investigated?

Fig. 315 illustrates four turns of a solenoid, and Fig. 316 represents a side view of the coil cut through the middle. In the top layer of wires the electrons are coming towards you and the field is clockwise. The electrons are going from you in the lower layer and the field is anti-clockwise (anti-corkscrew rule). The field

pattern is similar to the field of a bar magnet with its poles at A and B. *Is A a north or south pole? (2) What can you say about the field inside the solenoid? (3)*

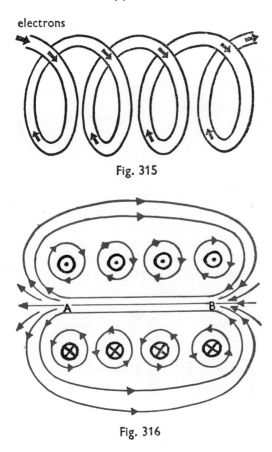

electrons

Fig. 315

Fig. 316

Experiment 14.2.

(a) Wind a 100 turn solenoid round an iron bar using 22 s.w.g. plastic covered wire. Wrap Sellotape round the solenoid and remove the iron bar. Suspend the solenoid from a wooden bar, using ½ in aluminium tape, and pass a current of several amperes through the coil. Bring a powerful magnet towards the solenoid as shown in Fig. 317. What happens? Reverse the magnet and note the result. Does the solenoid behave like a bar magnet?

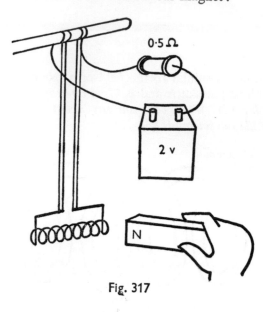

Fig. 317

(b) Now insert the iron bar into the solenoid and repeat the above experiment. What difference do you observe?

(c) Can you construct an electro-magnet using an iron nail and a length of wire? Try to find *two ways* of increasing the lifting power of this electro-magnet.

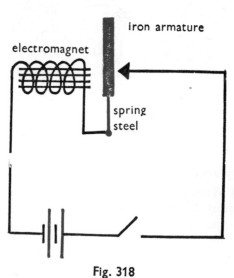

Fig. 318

An electro-magnet consists of a coil of wire wound round an iron core. Fig. 318 shows such a magnet used to operate a buzzer or electric bell. The spring steel holds the armature against the contact when the switch is open. *Can you explain how it operates when the switch is closed?* (4) Buzzer kits are available commercially[12].

Experiment 14.3. Wind a coil of 50 turns of 22 s.w.g. wire, and connect it through a switch to a 2 volt accumulator as shown in Fig. 319. Hang two 2 in nails side by side within the coil as shown. Can you explain what happens when the switch is closed?

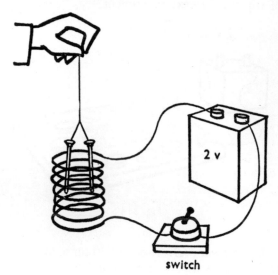

Fig. 319

When a ferromagnetic material is placed in a magnetic field the domains tend to line up with the field. The result is that the field becomes very much stronger. Powerful electro-magnets capable of lifting a man are available[20]. They require only a 1·5 volt dry cell to operate them.

Demonstration 14.4. Magnetising by a solenoid. Place an unmagnetised knitting needle into a solenoid and pass a direct current of several amperes through the coil. Remove the needle and test it to see if it is magnetised. Why is a *direct* current specifically stated?

Repeat this experiment using alternating instead of direct current and explain the result obtained. You should try this experiment several times to see if the results vary.

Demonstration 14.5. Demagnetising by a solenoid.

(*a*) Place a magnetised knitting needle into a solenoid and pass an alternating current through the coil. Slowly remove the needle along the axis of the solenoid to a distance of about 4 ft *while the current is flowing* and then switch off. Test the needle to see if it is a magnet.

(*b*) Alternatively, demagnetise the needle by gradually reducing the current to zero while the needle is inside the solenoid.

Measuring current

Experiment 14.6. Here is a model for you to build at home. Some wood, wire, cardboard and a nail are the main requirements. Can you make a railway signal which operates when a current flows through the coil? (Fig. 320). Can you explain how it works?

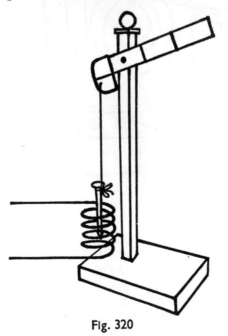

Fig. 320

A solenoid with electric current flowing through it behaves like a bar magnet, the strength of which depends on the current. It is therefore possible to use the force exerted by the coil on a bar magnet as a measure of the current passing through the coil. Such a device is called a *current balance.*

Experiment 14.7. A simple balance for measuring current may be constructed as follows. Wind 40 turns of 22 s.w.g. p.v.c. covered wire on to a $\frac{1}{2}$ in diameter former and mount it on a wood base as shown. A 14 in

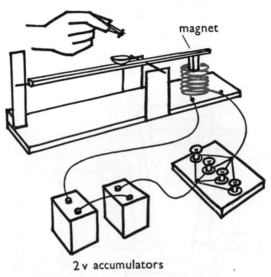

magnet

2 v accumulators

Fig. 321

length of $\frac{3}{16}$ in square balsa wood makes an ideal indicator. Glue a tiny strip of tin plate on one end of the balsa wood to hold a Ticonal E magnet (M2702)₉. Cut a section from a table tennis ball and glue it about 3 in from the same end to act as a balance pan. Push a needle through the strip so that it balances as shown in Fig. 321. Final adjustment may be made by moving the magnet to and fro on the tin plate. Similar current balances are available commercially₄.

Connect 4 bulb holders in parallel and wire them in series with the coil, two 2-volt accumulators and a switch. Screw one 3·5 volt 0·3 amp bulb into a holder, and place masses on the balance pan until the pointer returns to the original position. What do you do if the balance beam tips the wrong way? 1 cm lengths of p.v.c. covering from the 22 s.w.g. wire make suitable masses.

Note the number of masses required and repeat the procedure with 2, 3 and 4 bulbs in the circuit. Complete the following table of results.

Number of Bulbs (Current)	Number of masses (Force)
1	
2	
3	
4	

Construct a graph showing how the force changes with the current. How are they related?

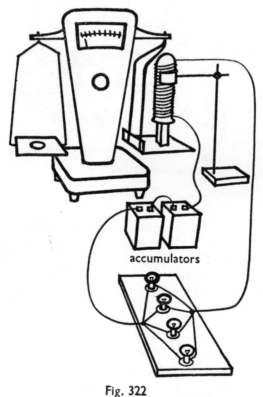

Fig. 322

Demonstration 14.8. An alternative way of showing the above relationship is to wind 70 turns of 22 s.w.g. wire on a 1 in diameter test tube and place it over an Alnico bar magnet resting on the pan of an Avery balance[22, 23].

Connect the circuit as shown and place masses on the left hand pan until the needle reads zero. Screw one bulb into a holder and switch on. Make sure that the current flows in such a direction as to push the scale pan down. Note the deflection. Repeat this procedure with 2, 3 and 4 bulbs.

Force on a conductor

In the current balance a force was exerted on a magnet which was situated in the field produced by an electric current. *Did the magnet exert a force on the coil?* (5) In the following experiments we will study the effect of passing a current through a conductor placed in the field of a permanent magnet.

Experiment 14.9. Pin a strip of $\frac{1}{2}$ in aluminium tape to two wooden blocks so that it is suspended between the poles of a large

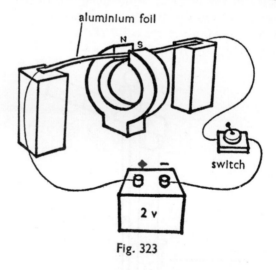

Fig. 323

horse-shoe magnet as shown in Fig. 323. Connect the ends of the foil to a d.c. source. What happens when the circuit is completed? If the arrangement is as shown in Fig. 323, does the foil move up or down? Reverse the cell connections and repeat the experiment.

Experiment 14.10. Barlow's wheel. In Barlow's wheel the current flows through one point of the star. This point lies between the poles of a strong horse-shoe magnet. Can you explain why the wheel rotates? Michael Faraday first obtained continuous rotation of a conductor in a magnetic field by using a similar arrangement. He used a disc instead of the star.

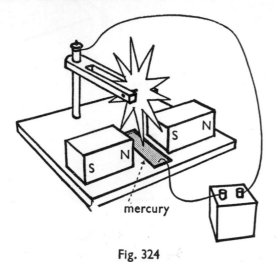

mercury

Fig. 324

Experiment 14.11.

(a) A round brass rod rests on two brass rails as shown in Fig. 325. The rod lies between the poles of a horse-shoe magnet. What is the relationship between the direction of the current, the field lines and the motion of the brass rod? What happens if the current is reversed?

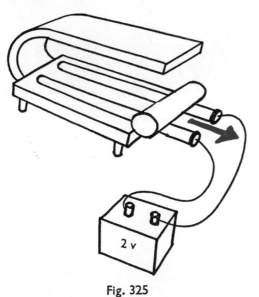

2 v

Fig. 325

(b) Here is an interesting variation of the above experiment. Several Magnadur magnets, with the same pole uppermost are fixed with Sellotape to a strip of wood. Two lengths of toy railway line fitted with insulating sleepers (Fig. 326) are then placed on top of them. If a brass roller is now placed on the rails, which are connected to a d.c. supply, the roller will accelerate along the line.

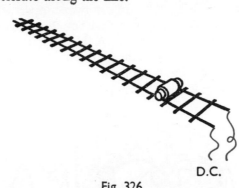

D.C.

Fig. 326

When current flows in a conductor lying in a magnetic field, the conductor moves at right angles to the field and at right angles to the direction of the current. There are many ways of remembering the direction of motion of the conductor in such a field: if you really *must* remember it! In practice you would probably switch on and see if it went up or down! Here is one suggestion.

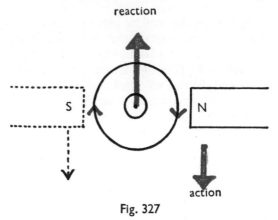

Fig. 327

As the field lines round the wire show the direction in which the *north pole* will tend to move (action), the reaction on the conductor must be in the opposite direction. The conductor will, therefore, be pushed in the direction indicated.

Electric motors

Experiment 14.12. Pour some concentrated copper sulphate solution into a glass dish placed between the poles of a horse-shoe magnet as shown in Fig. 328. Insert two copper wires in the positions shown and connect them to a 12 volt d.c. source. A little lycopodium powder sprinkled on the surface of the solution will make the motion of the liquid clearly visible. Why does the liquid move?

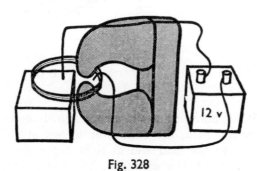

Fig. 328

Can you think of a way of modifying this liquid motor in order to make a metal disc rotate? What kind of metal would you use? Why?

If a rectangular coil is placed between the poles of a horse-shoe magnet as shown in Fig. 329(*a*) and (*b*) it will tend to move in the direction indicated. Having rotated through 90° to position (*c*) the coil will tend to stop. *Why? (6) Can you think of a way to cause the coil to rotate a further 180° assuming it overshot position (c) very slightly? (7) How could the coil be made to rotate continuously? (8)* To answer these questions you should build a simple electric motor.

Experiment 14.13. This motor may be constructed from a kit[11]. Two powerful Magnadur magnets are attached to a yoke of iron and a coil is placed between them (Fig. 330). Hold two wires as shown to feed the

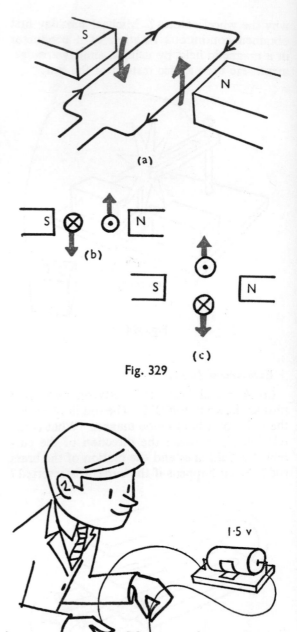

Fig. 329

Fig. 330

current from a 1·5 volt cell, via the commutator segments, to the coil. Can you arrange the wires so that the coil keeps turning? Kits to build rather more ambitious motors using electro-magnets instead of permanent magnets are also available$_{12}$.

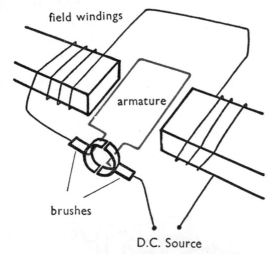

Fig. 331. Series Motor

In a 'real' electric motor the rotating coil is wound on a core made of many thin iron leaves or *laminations*. It is usually referred to as the *armature*. The permanent magnets are often replaced by electro-magnets, which are sometimes connected in series with the armature and sometimes in parallel. The wires which you held in contact with the commutator are called the *brushes*. In practice they are normally made of carbon. You should study a commercially built motor and try to identify the parts.

Dynamos

Oersted's discovery that a magnetic field was produced by an electric current led many people to ask if the reverse might also be true. Among them were Michael Faraday in Britain and Joseph Henry in America. Faraday kept a notebook in which he recorded material to be investigated. In 1822 he wrote in it 'convert magnetism into electricity'. Yet it was nine years later before he was able to detect such a current.

About the same time Henry was studying the same problem using electro-magnets. As insulated wire was almost unobtainable in those days, Henry is reported to have insulated some copper wire by using a number of silk ribbons obtained by 'the sacrifice on the part of his wife of her white petticoat'! Even this did not enable him to publish his results before Faraday's public announcement in 1831 of the discovery of electro-magnetic induction.

Experiment 14.14. Devise two experiments in which a micro-ammeter may be used to detect current (*a*) when a wire is made to move in a magnetic field and (*b*) when a bar magnet is thrust into a coil of wire. How may the strength and direction of the current be altered in each case?

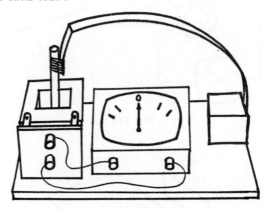

Fig. 332

Experiment 14.15. Attach a small bar magnet to the end of a piece of flexible steel strip. Allow the magnet to dip into a coil of about 100 turns as shown in Fig. 332. Use a centre-zero galvanometer (for example 1–0–1 mA) to indicate the current produced. What kind of current flows as the magnet vibrates up and down?

Experiment 14.16. Connect the terminals of a small d.c. electric motor to a sensitive voltmeter and rotate the motor spindle. How does the output vary as the speed of rotation increases?

An electric motor is an energy transformer. It transforms electric energy into mechanical energy. If, on the other hand, mechanical energy is fed into the motor, that is, if the armature is made to rotate, electrical energy is given out.

Demonstration 14.17. Use a steam engine to drive a model dynamo$_{33}$. When the engine speed is constant connect a torch bulb across the dynamo terminals. Does the engine speed alter? Why?

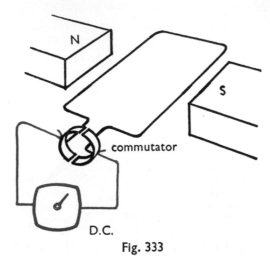

D.C.

Fig. 333

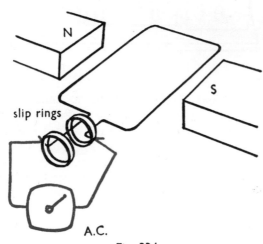

slip rings

A.C.

Fig. 334

A.C. and D.C.

Dynamos are of two main types: D.C. *generators* (Fig. 333) and A.C. generators or *alternators* (Fig. 334). In the case of the alternator, the current coming from the coil is fed to two brass rings on which the brushes press. The rings are called slip rings. We will see later in the course that there are many advantages to be gained by having electric current the direction of which is continually being reversed. *What is the frequency (number of to and fro current pulses per second) of the mains supply in Britain?* (9)

Experiment 14.18. Here is a simple alternator you can construct. It is similar in principle to a bicycle dynamo, and does not require slip rings as the coils do not rotate.

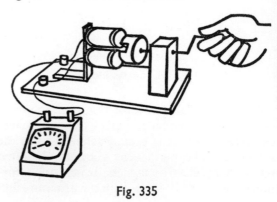

Fig. 335

Wind 100 turns on each limb of a U-shaped piece of soft iron. Alternatively, use the coils from an old electric bell. Mount an Eclipse pot magnet (833C) on a spindle as shown. The output may then be fed into an a.c. meter or a cathode ray oscilloscope. Use this alternator with and without its keeper. What difference does the keeper make? Why? How many factors can you find affecting the size of the e.m.f. and hence the current produced?

Visual aids

Charts

Science for Today. No. 14. Electricity in the Home[36]
The A.C. Electric Motor[37]
The Electric Generator[37]

Filmstrips

Electricity[44]

16 mm Sound Films

21.7365 The Story of Magnetism[44]
Magnetism[49]
A.C. and D.C.[49]
70.3579 Electro-magnetic Induction[44]

Suppliers

1. A. Young & Son Ltd., 57–61 Forrest Road, Edinburgh 1.
2. Philip Harris Ltd., 63 Ludgate Hill, Birmingham 3.
3. W. G. Pye & Co. Ltd., York Street, P.O. Box 60, Cambridge.
4. Griffin & George Ltd., Braeview Place, Nerston, East Kilbride.
   Griffin & George Ltd., Ealing Road, Alperton, Wembley, Middlesex.
5. Teltron Ltd., 239 Acton Lane, Chiswick, London W.4.
6. Radiospares Ltd., 4–8 Maple Street, London W.1.
7. Serinco, 6 Swan Place, Glenrothes, Fife.
8. E. J. Arnold & Sons Ltd., Butterley Street, Leeds 10.
9. Mullard Ltd., Components Division, Torrington Place, London W.C.1.
10. The International Nickel Company Ltd., Thames House, Millbank, London S.W.1.
11. Rollo Industries Ltd., St. Andrew's Works, Bonnybridge, Stirlingshire.
12. Precision Jigs Co. Ltd., 79 Caterham Avenue, Ilford, Essex.
13. Erie Resistor Ltd., South Denes, Great Yarmouth.
14. Rainbow Radio Ltd., Mincing Lane, Blackburn, Lancashire.
15. Morris Laboratory Instruments Ltd., The Tram Road, Folkestone, Kent.
16. W. B. Nicolson Ltd., Thornliebank Industrial Estate, Glasgow.
17. H. P. Freedman, 271–273 Archway Road, London N.6.
18. A. H. Baird Ltd., 33–39 Lothian Street, Edinburgh 1.
19. Dunlop Rubber Co. Ltd., Educational Section (S), 10–12 King Street, London S.W.1.
20. Cenco Instrumenten Mij. N.V., Konijnenberg 40, Breda, The Netherlands.
21. Gulton Industries Ltd., 21 Alva Street, Edinburgh 2.
22. L. Oertling Ltd., Cray Valley Works, St. Mary Cray, Orpington, Kent.
23. Stanton Instruments Ltd., 119 Oxford Street, Kingston-on-Thames.
24. Rotameter Manufacturing Co. Ltd., 330 Purley Way, Croydon, Surrey.
25. Hospital and Laboratory Supplies Ltd., 12 Charterhouse Square, London E.C.1.
26. Scientific Teaching Apparatus Ltd., Colquhoun House, 23–37 Broadwick Street, London W.1.
27. Advance Components Ltd., Roebuck Road, Hainault, Ilford, Essex.
28. A. R. Bolton & Co. Ltd., Bankhead Drive, Sighthill, Edinburgh 11.
29. Paton Hawksley Electronics Ltd., Rockhill Laboratories, Keynsham, Bristol.
30. The Irongate Co. Ltd., Irongate Wharf Road, Praed Street, London W.2.
31. Handy Angle Ltd., Reparco Works, Hamilton.
32. Dexion Ltd., Empire Way, Wembley Park, Middlesex.
33. Donray Models, 302 Morningside Road, Edinburgh 10.
34. Grayshaw Instruments, 126 Sandgate High Street, Folkestone, Kent.
35. Kodak Ltd., Kodak House, Kingsway, London.
36. Macmillan & Co. Ltd., St. Martins Street, London W.C.2.
37. Educational Productions Ltd., East Ardsley, Wakefield, Yorkshire.
38. George Philip & Sons Ltd., Victoria Road, London N.W.10.

39. Mullard Film Service, Mullard House, Torrington Place, London W.C.1.
40. Hugh Wood & Son Ltd., 23 Leman Street, London E.1.
41. Technicolor Ltd., Bath Road, Harmondsworth, West Drayton, Middlesex.
42. Central Film Library, Government Building, Bromyard Avenue, Acton, London W.3.
43. Educational Services Incorporated, 47 Galen Street, Watertown 72, Massachusetts, U.S.A.
44. Rank Film Library, 1 Aintree Road, Perivale, Greenford, Middlesex.
45. Nife Batteries, Redditch, Worcestershire.
46. I.C.I. Film Library, Imperial Chemical House, Millbank, London S.W.1.
47. Pictorial Charts Unit, 181 Uxbridge Road, London W.7.
48. Shell-Mex and B.P. Ltd., Public Relations Department (Films), Shell-Mex House, London W.C.2.
49. British Electrical Development Association, 2 Savoy Hill, London W.C.2.
50. E.F.V.A. Film Library, Brooklands House, Weybridge, Surrey.
51. Unicorn Head Visual Aids Ltd., 42 Westminster Palace Gardens, Victoria Street, London S.W.1.
52. Scottish Central Film Library, 16–17 Woodside Terrace, Charing Cross, Glasgow C.3.
53. Proops Bros. Ltd., 52 Tottenham Court Road, London W.1.

Index